SCIENCE IN EUROPE 1500–1800

Volume 1

A PRIMARY SOURCES ANTHOLOGY

SCIENCE IN EUROPE 1500–1800
Volume 1
A PRIMARY SOURCES ANTHOLOGY

Edited by Colin A. Russell

Contributors

Michael Bartholomew • Colin Chant • Noel Coley • David Goodman •
Peter Morris • Gerrylynn K. Roberts • Colin A. Russell

First published in 1991 by
The Open University
Walton Hall
Milton Keynes, MK7 6AA

Reprinted 1995 (with corrections); 1996

© 1996 The Open University

ISBN 0 7492 1100 8

Cover illustration: Frontispiece of Claude Perrault Mémoires pour servir à l'histoire naturelle des animaux, *1671 Paris. British Library c.l28.k.4 (1). (Reproduced by permission of the British Library Board.)*

This book forms part of an Open University course AS283: *The Rise of Scientific Europe, 1500–1800.* For information about this course please write to the Central Enquiry Service, The Open University, PO Box 200, Walton Hall, Milton Keynes, MK7 6YZ, UK.

Printed and bound in the United Kingdom by BPC Wheatons Ltd, Exeter.

1.3

Preface to the Primary Sources Anthology

To understand the rise of science in Europe, or any other series of events in history, it is clearly necessary to listen to the conclusions of people who have spent years reading and reflecting on the matter. The results of their labours can be invaluable, whether as popular accounts in the press, textbooks for students or learned monographs. Because they are written long after the events they describe such writings are often referred to as *secondary sources*. But historians who write them, and anyone else who needs to know more about the historical events in question, must, sooner or later, resort to documents of the time, contemporary records, the *primary sources*. There are many reasons for this.

Primary sources are uncorrupted by time (assuming they have survived in good environmental conditions). Even when they are torn, faded, covered with mildew or (as the antiquarian booksellers say) 'foxed in places', they may still be read with the aid of modern technology (such as ultra-violet lamps) and old-fashioned patience. Then they are also uncorrupted by the interpretations of later scholars, except in the rarest of cases where they have been deliberately tampered with; we receive them unfiltered by our predecessors or even contemporary colleagues. Above all, perhaps, they give us the authentic flavour and feel for the period in which they originated. To blow away the dust of ages from a letter or an old book is often to begin a process of discovery remarkably akin to that of the scientist in his or her laboratory. That at least is the testimony of those of us who have lived in both worlds.

Now it is of course a fact of life that most people have neither the time nor the opportunity to do much browsing amongst primary sources. Fortunately there is a solution to the problem. Thanks again to modern technology it becomes possible to do the next best thing, and that is to have in one's hands a reliable *copy* of a primary source. This can be on microfilm, on microfiche or (as here) on the printed page. It lacks the feel and smell of the original, but it is far more robust and can be treated with an abandon that, if applied to the original, would induce in a professional librarian or archivist the most serious signs of nervous protestation.

This collection relates to the events attending 'This rise of scientific Europe from 1500 to 1800'. It has been specially prepared to be part of an Open University undergraduate course with that title (Course AS283). A companion volume in the course is a *Secondary Sources Anthology*[1] and there are also television and audio-visual components. The kernel of the course is a textbook (or 'Course

[1] David Goodman (ed.) (1991) *Science in Europe, 1500–1800: A Secondary Sources Anthology.* Milton Keynes: The Open University.

Book')[2] and students are assisted through all the material by a comprehensive Study Guide. The material is grouped into chapters corresponding to the chapters of the Course Book and has in most cases been chosen by the authors of those chapters. While it is essential reading for this particular course the collection is rich and diverse enough to be of wide interest to anyone concerned with the broader aspects of history of science and with the fundamental changes in our world since Copernicus proposed that it was not, after all, at the geometrical centre of the universe.

To my six colleagues in the Department of History and Science and Technology who are also my co-authors I am very grateful, and not merely for their suggestions for this anthology. My thanks also go to Keith Whettam, the copy editor. It is also a pleasure to thank Anne Bullman, the Course Co-ordinator, for a great deal of hard administrative work connected with this book as well as many other aspects of the course. Successfully to co-ordinate the efforts of seven strong-minded academics, and to keep them to their deadlines, is no mean feat. She has performed it with exemplary grace and skill.

Colin A. Russell

[2] David Goodman and Colin A. Russell (eds) (1991) *The Rise of Scientific Europe, 1500–1800*, Milton Keynes: The Open University; and London: Hodder and Stoughton.

Contents

Chapter 1: Europe's awakening

1.1 Georg Agricola, *De Re Metallica*, 1556   1

Chapter 2: Copernicus and his revolution

2.1 Prefaces from Copernicus's *De Revolutionibus*, 1543   6
2.2 The new astronomy: extract from G. J. Rheticus, *Holy Scripture and the Motion of the Earth*, c.1540   10
2.3 Christopher Marlow, *The Tragedy of Dr. Faustus*, 1604   16

Chapter 3: The spread of Copernicanism in northern Europe

3.1 Edward Wright, 'Laudatory address' in William Gilbert, *De Magnete*   18
3.2 J. Kepler, *Astronomia Nova*, Heidelberg, 1609   22
3.3 John Donne, 'First Anniversarie', 1611   24
3.4 John Wilkins, *A Discourse concerning a New Planet*, London, 1640   25
3.5 J. Kepler, *Harmonices Mundi*, 1619   27

Chapter 4: Crisis in Italy

4.1 Letter from Galileo to Grand Duchess Christina, 1615   33
4.2 Letter from Cardinal Bellarmino to Paolo Foscarini, 12 April 1615   37
4.3 Trans. of MS G3 in Archive of the Sacred Congregation for the Doctrine of the Faith   38

Chapter 5: Iberian science: Navigation, empire and counter-reformation

5.1 Garcia d'Orta, *Colloquies on the Simples and Drugs of India*   41
5.2 Nicolás Monardes, *La Historia Medicinal de las cosas que se traen de nuestras Indias Occidentales que sirven en Medicina*   44
5.3 Diego de Zúñiga, *In Job commentaria*   45
5.4 Diego de Zúñiga, *Philosophia prima pars*   46
5.5 Gaspar de Quiroga, *Index et Catalogus Librorum prohibitorum*   46

Chapter 6: Science from the Earth in central Europe

6.1 Ulrich Rülein von Calw, 'On the Origin of Metals', from *Ein nützlich Bergbüchlein*, c.1500   48
6.2 Georgius Agricola, 'On the Origin of Metals', from *De Ortu et Causis Subterraneorum*, 1546   49
6.3 Georgius Agricola, 'On the Knowledge of the Miner', from Book I of *De Re Metallica*, 1556   50
6.4 Georgius Agricola, 'On Assaying', from Book VII of *De Re Metallica*, 1556   51

6.5 Paracelsus, 'Man and His Body', from Jolande Jacobi (ed.),
     Paracelsus: Selected Writings   52
6.6 Paracelsus, 'The Physician's Remedies', from Jolande Jacobi (ed.),
     Paracelsus: Selected Writings   53
6.7 Paracelsus, 'Alchemy, Art of Transformation', from Jolande Jacobi
     (ed.), *Paracelsus: Selected Writings*   55

Chapter 7: French science in the seventeenth century

7.1 R. Descartes, *Discourse on Method*   58
7.2 C. Glaser, 'The purpose of early chemistry', *Traité de la Chimie*,
     Paris, 1663   60
7.3 B. Pascal, *Story of the Great Experiment on the Equilibrium of Fluids*,
     1648   63

Chapter 8: Science in seventeenth-century England

8.1 W. Gilbert, *De Magnete*, 1600   65
8.2 W. Harvey, *De motu cordis*, 1626   68
8.3 R. Boyle, *Of the Excellency and Grounds of the Corpuscular
     Philosophy*, London, 1674   70
8.4 I. Newton, *Opticks*   73

Chapter 9: Scientific academies across Europe

9.1 'Introduction to the *Saggi* of the Accademia del Cimento', 1667   79
9.2 'On the History of the Royal Society: The Preface and Design of
     this Discourse', from Thomas Sprat, *History of the Royal Society*,
     1667   83
9.3 'On the History of the Royal Society: A Model of their Whole
     Design', from Thomas Sprat, *History of the Royal Society*, 1667   84
9.4 'On the History of the Royal Society: Their Course of Inquiry',
     from Thomas Sprat, *History of the Royal Society*, 1667   86

Chapter 10: The reception of Newtonianism in Europe

10.1 W. J. 'sGravesande, *Mathematical Elements of Natural Philosophy*   90
10.2 Ephraim Chambers, *Cyclopedia*, London, 1728   94

Chapter 11: Science in the Scottish Enlightenment

11.1 Extract from J. Hutton, *Abstract of a dissertation read in the Royal
      Society of Edinburgh . . . concerning the system of the earth, its
      duration and stability*   101
11.2 Joseph Black, 'Experiments upon Magnesia Alba, Quicklime and
      some other Alkaline Substances', *Essays and Observations, Physical
      and Literary*   104
11.3 Adam Smith, *Essays on Philosophical Subjects*   110

Chapter 12: Science on the fringe of Europe: Eighteenth-century Sweden

12.1 A. Celsius, 'A barometrical experiment', *Phil. Trans.*, 1724   112

12.2 Lecture Advertisement for M. Triewald, 1725: National Library
   of Scotland   113
12.3 P. Wargentin, 'On the variation of the magnetic needle'   114
12.4 C. Linnaeus, Dedication and Preface to *Species Plantarum*, 1753 114
12.5 T. Bergman, 'Observations on electricity, and on a thunder-storm' 118
12.6 P. Wargentin, 'Observations on the same transit [of Venus]; and
   on an eclipse of the moon'   118
12.7 C. W. Scheele, *Chemische Abhandlung von der Luft und dem Feuer* 120
12.8 E. D. Clarke, *Travels in various parts of Europe, Asia and Africa* 123

Chapter 13: Science in orthodox Europe

13.1 *Letters of Euler to a German Princess*   127
13.2 S. P. Krasheninnikov, *The History of Kamtschatka*   129
13.3 Mikhail Lomonosov, *The Appearance of Venus on the Sun, Observed
   at the St. Petersburg Academy of Sciences on the 26th Day of May in
   the Year 1761*   134

Chapter 14: Establishing science in eighteenth-century central Europe

14.1 Robert Jameson, 'On the Supposed Existence of Mechanical
   Deposits and Petrefactions in the Primitive Mountains, and an
   Account of Petrefactions which have been discovered in the
   newest Flötz Trapp Formation', 1802   138

Chapter 15: The chemical revolution in four countries

15.1 S. Hales, *Vegetable Staticks*   147
15.2 J. Priestley, *Experiments and Observations on Different Kinds of Air* 150
15.3 A. L. Lavoisier, *Elements of Chemistry*   153

Chapter 1: Europe's awakening

1.1 Georg Agricola, *De Re Metallica*, 1556,
Hoover translation, 1912; Dover reprint, 1950. Preface,
pp. xxv–xxxi

TO THE MOST ILLUSTRIOUS
AND MOST MIGHTY DUKES OF
Saxony, Landgraves of Thuringia, Margraves of Meissen,
Imperial Overlords of Saxony, Burgraves of Altenberg
and Magdeburg, Counts of Brena, Lords of
Pleissnerland, To MAURICE Grand Marshall
and Elector of the Holy Roman Empire
and to his brother AUGUSTUS,

GEORGE AGRICOLA S.D.

Most illustrious Princes, often have I considered the metallic arts as a whole, as Moderatus Columella[1] considered the agricultural arts, just as if I had been considering the whole of the human body; and when I had perceived the various parts of the subject, like so many members of the body, I became afraid that I might die before I should understand its full extent, much less before I could immortalise it in writing. This book itself indicates the length and breadth of the subject, and the number and importance of the sciences of which at least some little knowledge is necessary to miners. Indeed, the subject of mining is a very extensive one, and one very difficult to explain; no part of it is fully dealt with by the Greek and Latin authors whose works survive; and since the art is one of the most ancient, the most necessary and the most profitable to mankind, I considered that I ought not to neglect it. Without doubt, none of the arts is older than agriculture, but that of the metals is not less ancient; in fact they are at least equal and coeval, for no mortal man ever tilled a field without implements. In truth, in all the works of agriculture, as in the other arts, implements are used which are made from metals, or which could not be made without the use of metals; for this reason the metals are of the greatest necessity to man. When an art is so poor that it lacks metals, it is not of much importance, for nothing is made without tools. Besides, of all ways whereby great wealth is acquired by good and honest means, none is more advantageous than mining; for although

---

[1] Lucius Junius Moderatus was a Roman, a native of Cadiz, and lived during the 1st century. He was the author of *De Re Rustica* in twelve volumes. It was first printed in 1472, and some fifteen or sixteen editions had been printed before Agricola's death.

from fields which are well tilled (not to mention other things) we derive rich yields, yet we obtain richer products from mines; in fact, one mine is often much more beneficial to us than many fields. For this reason we learn from the history of nearly all ages that very many men have been made rich by the mines, and the fortunes of many kings have been much amplified thereby. But I will not now speak more of these matters, because I have dealt with these subjects partly in the first book of this work, and partly in the other work entitled *De Veteribus et Novis Metallis*, where I have refuted the charges which have been made against metals and against miners. Now, though the art of husbandry, which I willingly rank with the art of mining, appears to be divided into many branches, yet it is not separated into so many as this art of ours, nor can I teach the principles of this as easily as Columella did of that. He had at hand many writers upon husbandry whom he could follow,—in fact, there are more than fifty Greek authors whom Marcus Varro enumerates, and more than ten Latin ones, whom Columella himself mentions. I have only one whom I can follow; that is C. Plinius Secundus, and he expounds only a very few methods of digging ores and of making metals. Far from the whole of the art having been treated by any one writer, those who have written occasionally on any one or another of its branches have not even dealt completely with a single one of them. Moreover, there is a great scarcity even of these, since alone of all the Greeks, Strato of Lampsacus, the successor of Theophrastus, wrote a book on the subject, *De Machinis Metallicis*; except, perhaps a work by the poet Philo, a small part of which embraced to some degree the occupation of mining. Pherecrates seems to have introduced into his comedy, which was similar in title, miners as slaves or as persons condemned to serve in the mines. Of the Latin writers, Pliny, as I have already said, has described a few methods of working. Also among the authors I must include the modern writers, whosoever they are, for no one should escape just condemnation who fails to award due recognition to persons whose writings he uses, even very slightly. Two books have been written in our tongue; the one on the assaying of mineral substances and metals, somewhat confused, whose author is unknown; the other 'On Veins,' of which Pandulfus Anglus is also said to have written, although the German book was written by Calbus of Freiberg, a well-known doctor; but neither of them accomplished the task he had begun. Recently Vannucci Biringuccio, of Sienna, a wise man experienced in many matters, wrote in vernacular Italian on the subject of the melting, separating, and alloying of metals. He touched briefly on the methods of smelting certain ores, and explained more fully the methods of making certain juices; by reading his directions, I have refreshed my memory of those things which I myself saw in Italy; as for many matters on which I write, he did not touch upon them at all, or touched but lightly. This book was given me by Franciscus Badoarius, a Patrician of Venice, and a man of wisdom and of repute; this he had promised that he would do, when in the previous year he was at Marienberg, having been sent by the Venetians as an Ambassador to King Ferdinand. Beyond these books I do not find any writings on the metallic arts. For that reason, even if the book of Strato existed, from all these sources not one-half of the whole body of the science of mining could be pieced together.

Seeing that there have been so few who have written on the subject of the metals, it appears to me all the more wonderful that so many alchemists have arisen who would compound metals artifically, and who would change one into another. Hermolaus Barbarus, a man of high rank and station, and distinguished in all kinds of learning, has mentioned the names of many in his writings; and I will proffer more, but only famous ones, for I will limit myself to a few. Thus Osthanes has written on χυμευτικά; and there are Hermes; Chanes; Zosimus, the Alexandrian, to his sister Theosebia; Olympiodorus, also an Alexandrian; Agathodæmon; Democritus, not the one of Abdera, but some other whom I know not; Orus Chrysorichites, Pebichius, Comerius, Joannes, Apulejus, Petasius, Pelagius, Africanus, Theophilus, Synesius, Stephanus to Heracleus Cæsar, Heliodorus to Theodosius, Geber, Callides Rachaidibus, Veradianus, Rodianus, Canides, Merlin, Raymond Lully, Arnold de Villa Nova, and Augustinus Pantheus of Venice; and three women, Cleopatra, the maiden Taphnutia, and Maria the Jewess. All these alchemists employ obscure language, and Johanes Aurelius Augurellus of Rimini, alone has used the language of poetry. There are many other books on this subject, but all are difficult to follow, because the writers upon these things use strange names, which do not properly belong to the metals, and because some of them employ now one name and now another, invented by themselves, though the thing itself changes not. These masters teach their disciples that the base metals, when smelted, are broken up; also they teach the methods by which they reduce them to the primary parts and remove whatever is superfluous in them, and by supplying what is wanted make out of them the precious metals—that is, gold and silver,—all of which they carry out in a crucible. Whether they can do these things or not I cannot decide; but, seeing that so many writers assure us with all earnestness that they have reached that goal for which they aimed, it would seem that faith might be placed in them; yet also seeing that we do not read of any of them ever having become rich by this art, nor do we now see them growing rich, although so many nations everywhere have produced, and are producing, alchemists, and all of them are straining every nerve night and day to the end that they may heap a great quantity of gold and silver, I should say the matter is dubious. But although it may be due to carelessness of the writers that they have not transmitted to us the names of the masters who acquired great wealth through this occupation, certainly it is clear that their disciples either do not understand their precepts or, if they do understand them, do not follow them; for if they do comprehend them, seeing that these disciples have been and are so numerous, they would have by to-day filled whole towns with gold and silver. Even their books proclaim their vanity, for they inscribe in them the names of Plato and Aristotle and other philosophers, in order that such high-sounding inscriptions may impose upon simple people and pass for learning. There is another class of alchemists who do not change the substance of base metals, but colour them to represent gold or silver, so that they appear to be that which they are not, and when this appearance is taken from them by the fire, as if it were a garment foreign to them, they return to their own character. These alchemists, since they deceive people, are not only held in the greatest odium, but their frauds are a capital offence. No less a fraud, warranting capital punishment, is committed by a third sort of alchemists; these throw into a crucible a small piece of gold or silver hidden in a coal, and after mixing therewith fluxes which have the power of extracting it, pretend to be making gold from orpiment, or silver from tin and like substances. But concerning the art of alchemy, if it be an art, I will speak further elsewhere. I will now return to the art of mining.

Since no authors have written of this art in its entirety, and since foreign nations and races do not understand our tongue, and, if they did understand it, would be able to learn only a small part of the art through the works of those authors whom we do possess, I have written these twelve books *De Re Metallica*. Of these, the first book contains the arguments which may be used against this art, and against metals and the mines, and what can be said in their favour. The second book describes the miner, and branches into a discourse on the finding of veins. The third book deals with veins and stringers, and seams in the rocks. The fourth books explains the method of delimiting veins, and also describes the functions of the mining officials. The fifth book describes the digging of ore and the surveyor's art. The sixth book describes the miners' tools and machines. The seventh book is on the assaying of ore. The eighth book lays down the rules for the work of roasting, crushing, and washing the ore. The ninth book explains the methods of smelting ores. The tenth book instructs those who are studious of the metallic arts in the work of separating silver from gold, and lead from gold and silver. The eleventh book shows the way of separating silver from copper. The twelfth book gives us rules for manufacturing salt, soda, alum, vitriol, sulphur, bitumen, and glass.

Although I have not fulfilled the task which I have undertaken, on account of the great magnitude of the subject, I have, at all events, endeavoured to fulfil it, for I have devoted much labour and care, and have even gone to some expense upon it; for with regard to the veins, tools, vessels, sluices, machines, and furnaces, I have not only described them, but have also hired illustrators to delineate their forms, lest descriptions which are conveyed by words should either not be understood by men of our own times, or should cause difficulty to posterity, in the same way as to us difficulty is often caused by many names which the Ancients (because such words were familiar to all of them) have handed down to us without any explanation.

I have omitted all those things which I have not myself seen, or have not read or heard of from persons upon whom I can rely. That which I have neither seen, nor carefully considered after reading or hearing of, I have not written about. The same rule must be understood with regard to all my instruction, whether I enjoin things which ought to be done, or describe things which are usual, or condemn things which are done. Since the art of mining does not lend itself to elegant language, these books of mine are correspondingly lacking in refinement of style. The things dealt with in this art of metals sometimes lack names, either because they are new, or because, even if they are old, the record of the names by which they were formerly known has been lost. For this reason I have been forced by a necessity, for which I must be pardoned, to describe some of them by a number of words combined, and to distinguish others by new names,— to which latter class belong *Ingestor, Discretor, Lotor,* and *Excoctor.* Other things, again, I have alluded to by old names such as the *Cisium,* for when Nonius Marcellus wrote, this was the name of a two-wheeled vehicle, but I have adopted it for a small vehicle which has only one wheel; and if anyone does not approve of these names, let him either find more appropriate ones for these things, or discover the words used in the writings of the Ancients.

These books, most illustrious Princes, are dedicated to you for many reasons, and above all others, because metals have proved of the greatest value to you; for though your ancestors drew rich profits from the revenues of their vast and wealthy territories, and likewise from the taxes which were paid by the foreigners by way of toll and by the natives by way of tithes, yet they drew far richer profits from the mines. Because of the mines not a few towns have risen into eminence, such as Freiberg, Annaberg, Marienberg, Schneeberg, Geyer, and Altenberg, not to mention others. Nay, if I understand anything, greater wealth now lies hidden beneath the ground in the mountainous parts of your territory than is visible and apparent above ground. Farewell.

    Chemnitz, Saxony,
      December First, 1550

Chapter 2: Copernicus and his revolution

2.1 Prefaces from Copernicus's *De Revolutionibus*, 1543; from *Great Books of the World*, vol. 16, 1952, pp. 505–9. Chicago: Encyclopaedia Britannica Inc.

To the Reader Concerning the Hypotheses of this Work

Since the newness of the hypotheses of this work—which sets the earth in motion and puts an immovable sun at the centre of the universe—has already received a great deal of publicity, I have no doubt that certain of the savants have taken grave offense and think it wrong to raise any disturbance among liberal disciplines which have had the right set-up for a long time now. If, however, they are willing to weigh the matter scrupulously, they will find that the author of this work has done nothing which merits blame. For it is the job of the astronomer to use painstaking and skilled observation in gathering together the history of the celestial movements, and then—since he cannot by any line of reasoning reach the true causes of these movements—to think up or construct whatever causes or hypotheses he pleases such that, by the assumption of these causes, those same movements can be calculated from the principles of geometry for the past and for the future too. This artist is markedly outstanding in both of these respects: for it is not necessary that these hypotheses should be true, or even probably; but it is enough if they provide a calculus which fits the observations—unless by some chance there is anyone so ignorant of geometry and optics as to hold the epicycle of Venus as probable and to believe this to be a cause why Venus alternately precedes and follows the sun at an angular distance of up to 40° or more. For who does not see that it necessarily follows from this assumption that the diameter of the planet in its perigee should appear more than four times greater, and the body of the planet more than sixteen times greater, than in its apogee? Nevertheless the experience of all the ages is opposed to that. There are also other things in this discipline which are just as absurd, but it is not necessary to examine them right now. For it is sufficiently clear that this art is absolutely and profoundly ignorant of the causes of the apparent irregular movements. And if it constructs and thinks up causes—and it has certainly thought up a good many—nevertheless it does not think them up in order to persuade anyone of their truth but only in order that they may provide a correct basis for calculation. But since for one and the same movement varying hypotheses are proposed from time to time, as eccentricity or epicycle for the movement of the sun, the astronomer much prefers to take the one which is easiest to grasp. Maybe the philosopher demands probability instead; but neither of them will grasp anything certain or hand it on, unless it has been divinely revealed to him. Therefore let us permit these

6

new hypotheses to make a public appearance among old ones which are themselves no more probable, especially since they are wonderful and easy and bring with them a vast storehouse of learned observations. And as far as hypotheses go, let no one expect anything in the way of certainty from astronomy, since astronomy can offer us nothing certain, lest, if anyone take as true that which has been constructed for another use, he go away from this discipline a bigger fool than when he came to it. Farewell.

Preface and Dedication to Pope Paul III

[ii^b] I can reckon easily enough, Most Holy Father, that as soon as certain people learn that in these books of mine which I have written about the revolutions of the spheres of the world I attribute certain motions to the terrestrial globe, they will immediately shout to have me and my opinion hooted off the stage. For my own works do not please me so much that I do not weigh what judgments others will pronounce concerning them. And although I realize that the conceptions of a philosopher are placed beyond the judgment of the crowd, because it is his loving duty to seek the truth in all things, in so far as God has granted that to human reason; nevertheless I think we should avoid opinions utterly foreign to rightness. And when I considered how absurd this 'lecture' would be held by those who know that the opinion that the Earth rests immovable in the middle of the heavens as if their centre had been confirmed by the judgments of many ages—if I were to assert to the contrary that the Earth moves; for a long time I was in great difficulty as to whether I should bring to light my commentaries written to demonstrate the Earth's movement, or whether it would not be better to follow the example of the Pythagoreans and certain others who used to hand down the mysteries of their philosophy not in writing but by word of mouth and only to their relatives and friends—witness the letter of Lysis to Hipparchus. They however seem to me to have done that not, as some judge, out of a jealous unwillingness to communicate their doctrines but in order that things of very great beauty which have been investigated by the loving care of great men should not be scorned by those who find it a bother to expend any great energy on letters—except on the money-making variety—or who are provoked by the exhortations and examples of others to the liberal study of philosophy but on account of their natural [iii^a] stupidity hold the position among philosophers that drones hold among bees. Therefore, when I weighed these things in my mind, the scorn which I had to fear on account of the newness and absurdity of my opinion almost drove me to abandon a work already undertaken.

But my friends made me change my course in spite of my long-continued hesitation and even resistance. First among them was Nicholas Schonberg, Cardinal of Capua, a man distinguished in all branches of learning; next to him was my devoted friend Tiedeman Giese, Bishop of Culm, a man filled with the greatest zeal for the divine and liberal arts: for he in particular urged me frequently and even spurred me on by added reproaches into publishing this book and letting come to light a work which I had kept hidden among my things for not merely nine years, but for almost four times nine years. Not a few other learned and distinguished men demanded the same thing of me, urging me to refuse no longer—on account of the fear which I felt—to contribute my work to the common utility of those who are really interested in mathematics: they said that the absurder my teaching about the movement of the Earth now seems to very many persons, the more wonder and thanksgiving will it be the object of, when after the publication of my commentaries those same persons see the fog of absurdity dissipated by my luminous demonstrations. Accordingly I was led by such persuasion and by that hope finally to permit my friends to undertake the publication of a work which they had long sought from me.

But perhaps Your Holiness will not be so much surprised at my giving the results of my nocturnal study to the light—after having taken such care in working them out that I did not hesitate to put in writing my conceptions as to the movement of the Earth—as you will be eager to hear from me what came into my mind that in opposition to the general opinion of mathematicians and almost in opposition to common sense I should dare to imagine some movement of the Earth. And so I am unwilling to hide from Your Holiness that nothing except my knowledge that mathematicians have not agreed with one another in their researches moved me to think out a different scheme of drawing up the movements of the spheres of the world. For in the first place mathematicians are so uncertain about the movements of the sun and moon that they can neither demonstrate nor observe the unchanging magnitude of the revolving year. Then in setting up the solar and lunar movements and those of the other five wandering stars, they do not employ the same principles, assumptions, or demonstrations for the revolutions and apparent movements. For some make use of homocentric circles only, others of eccentric circles and epicycles, by means of which however they do not fully attain what they seek. For although those who have put their trust in homocentric circles have shown that various different movements can be composed of such circles, nevertheless they have not been able to establish anything for certain that would fully correspond to the phenomena. But even if those who have thought up eccentric circles seem to have been able for the most part to compute the apparent movements numerically by those means, they have in the meanwhile admitted a great deal which seems to contradict the first principles of regularity of movement. Moreover, they have not been able to discover or to infer the chief point of all, i.e., the form of the world and the certain commensurability of its parts. But they are in exactly the same fix as someone taking from different places hands, feet, head, and the other limbs—shaped very beautifully but not with reference to one body and without correspondence to one another—so that such parts made up a monster rather than a man. And so, in the process of demonstration which they call 'method,' they are found either to have omitted something necessary or to have admitted something foreign which by no means pertains to the matter; and they would by no means have been in this fix, if they had followed sure principles. For if the hypotheses they assumed were not false, everything which followed from the hypotheses would have been verified without fail; and though what I am saying may be obscure right now, nevertheless it will become clearer in the proper place.

Accordingly, when I had meditated upon this lack of certitude in the traditional mathematics concerning the composition of movements of the spheres of the world, I began to be annoyed that the philosophers, who in other respects had made a very careful scrutiny of the least details of the world, had discovered no sure scheme for the movements of the machinery of the world, which has been built for us by the Best and Most Orderly Workman of all. Wherefore I took the trouble to reread all the books by philosophers which I could get hold of, to see if any of them even supposed that the movements of the spheres of the world were different from those laid down by those who taught mathematics in the schools. And as a matter of fact, I found first in Cicero that Nicetas thought that the Earth moved. And afterwards I found in Plutarch that there were some others of the same opinion: I shall copy out his words here, so that they may be known to all:

> Some think that the Earth is at rest; but Philolaus the Pythagorean says that it moves around the fire with an obliquely circular motion, like the sun and moon. Herakleides of Pontus and Ekphantus the Pythagorean do not give the Earth any movement of locomotion, but rather a limited movement of rising and setting around its centre, like a wheel.

Therefore I also, having found occasion, began to meditate upon the mobility of the Earth. And although the opinion seemed absurd, nevertheless because I knew that others before me had been granted the liberty of constructing whatever circles they pleased in order to demonstrate astral phenomena, I thought that I too would be readily permitted to test whether or not, by the laying down that the Earth had some movement, demonstrations less shaky than those of my predecessors could be found for the revolutions of the celestial spheres.

And so, having laid down the movements which I attribute to the Earth farther on in the work, I finally discovered by the help of long and numerous observations that if the movements of the other wandering stars are correlated with the circular movement of the Earth, and if the movements are computed in accordance with the revolution of each planet, not only do all their phenomena follow from that but also this correlation binds together so closely the order and magnitudes of all the planets and of their spheres or orbital circles and the heavens themselves that nothing can be shifted around in any part of them without disrupting the remaining parts and the universe as a whole.

Accordingly, in composing my work I adopted the following order: in the first book I describe all the locations of the spheres or orbital circles together with the movements which I attribute to the earth, so that this book contains as it were the general set-up of the universe. But afterwards in the remaining books I correlate all the movements of the other planets and their spheres or orbital circles with the mobility of the Earth, so that it can be gathered from that how far the apparent movements of the remaining planets and their orbital circles can be saved by being correlated with the movements of the Earth. And I have no doubt that talented and learned mathematicians will agree with me, if—as philosophy demands in the first place—they are willing to give not superficial but profound thought and effort to what I bring forward in this work in demonstrating these things. And in order that the unlearned as well as the learned might see that I was not seeking to flee from the judgment of any man, I preferred to dedicate these results of my nocturnal study to Your Holiness rather than to anyone else; because, even in this remote corner of the earth where I live, you are held to be most eminent both in the dignity of your order and in your love of letters and even of mathematics; hence, by the authority of your judgment you can easily provide a guard against the bites of slanderers, despite the proverb that there is no medicine for the bite of a sycophant.

But if perchance there are certain 'idle talkers' who take it upon themselves to pronounce judgment, although wholly ignorant of mathematics, and if by shamelessly distorting the sense of some passage in Holy Writ to suit their purpose, they dare to reprehend and to attack my work; they worry me so little that I shall even scorn their judgments as foolhardy. For it is not unknown that Lactantius, otherwise a distinguished writer but hardly a mathematician, speaks in an utterly childish fashion concerning the shape of the Earth, when he laughs at those who have affirmed that the Earth has the form of a globe. And so the studious need not be surprised if people like that laugh at us. Mathematics is written for mathematicians; and among them, if I am not mistaken, my labours will be seen to contribute something to the ecclesiastical commonwealth, the principate of which Your Holiness now holds. For not many years ago under Leo X when the Lateran Council was considering the question of reforming the Ecclesiastical Calendar, no decision was reached, for the sole reason that the magnitude of the year and the months and the movements of the sun and moon had not yet been measured with sufficient accuracy. From that time on I gave attention to making more exact observations of these things and was encouraged to do so by that most distinguished man, Paul, Bishop of Fossombrone, who had been present at those deliberations. But what have I accomplished in this matter I leave to the judgment of Your Holiness in particular and to that of all other learned mathematicians. And so as not to appear to Your Holiness to make more promises concerning the utility of this book than I can fulfill, I now pass on to the body of the work.

2.2 The new astronomy: extract from G. J. Rheticus, *Holy Scripture and the Motion of the Earth;* c.1540; trans. R. Hooykaas, from *G. J. Rheticus' Treatise on Holy Scripture and the Motion of the Earth,* 1984, pp. 91–101. Amsterdam: North-Holland Pub. Co.

Furthermore, there will not be lacking those who will bellow that it is monstrous to attribute movements to the earth, and who will take occasion to draw on and display their wisdom taken from the philosophers of nature. They are ridiculous, as if God's power could be measured by our force or our intellect. Are we to think that anything is impossible for God, Who, by His Word, made the whole natural order out of nothing? Are we to tie God to the disputations of the Peripatetics about the heavy and the light, Him Who is tied to no place, but Who fills the whole world and is everywhere present and powerful, and Who places the Antipodes firmly on the earth? And He Who decreed that heaven should everywhere be above, is He unable to give the earth natural movements in accord with its shape? Not in any way, in my opinion. Nor therefore is it necessary for us to agree with Aristotle, when he teaches that movements from the centre, to the centre, and around the centre are distinct from each other. We may indeed rightly insist, especially as mathematical reasoning compels us, that the whole earth moves in a circle, and that therefore this motion is present in all its parts. Furthermore, that motions from the centre and to the centre appear by accident in the elements, as when air, confined by water or earth, tends upwards, and breaks out towards the place, which nature has assigned to it, and earth that has been thrown up into the air, keeps falling downward, until it stops on the earth, or occupies the centre of the earth, that being its naturally allotted place. Wherefore we would say that to bring something into its place is nothing else than to bring it into its proper 'Form', and that the ancients rightly held—in opposition to Aristotle—that like is attracted by like. For this is the reason and divine ordinance, on account of which the Sun, the Moon, the stars, and the earth are spherical, *and it is not proved that heavy objects tend to reach the centre of the universe, but only towards the centre of their own globe.*

Indeed, if we are referred back to Holy Scripture, and someone first interprets what we have adduced about the mobility of the earth in some other way, and then alleges other passages of Scripture by which he asserts the earth's immobility, and shows the movements assigned to the Sun by God . . . As to his first point I will not spend much time in arguing with him, although the passages we have cited seem clear enough, and it would be easy to refute objections possible to find there. For we have not made those suggestions from eagerness to affirm them, but from a desire to investigate,—in this matter following, so far as our mediocrity allows, in the footsteps of St. Augustine. And we also have to take note of the fact that the Holy Spirit has not wished to compose a course of Physics, but rather a rule of life, and to teach how we may be made children of God.

Now, the passages of Scripture, which occur to us as the principal ones against the mobility of the earth, are roughly these: Isaiah 42: 'Thus says the Lord God who creates the heavens and spreads them out, who settles the earth and the things which grow out of it, giving breath to the people which is on it, and His Spirit to those who walk upon it'. Likewise, chap. 44: 'I am the Lord, who makes all things, spreading out the heavens and settling the earth, I alone and none with Me'. And later, chap. 48: 'My hand also has founded the earth, and My right hand has spanned the heavens'. David, Ps. 92: 'For He has so established the earth that it shall not be moved'.

Ps. 101: 'In the beginning Thou, Lord, hast founded the earth, and the heavens are the work of Thy hands'.

Ps. 103: 'Who hast founded the earth on its foundations. It will not be shaken for ever'.

Ps. 118: 'Thy verity is from generation to generation; Thou hast founded the earth, and it abides'.

Zacharias, ch. 12: '(Thus) said the Lord who spreads out the heavens, who founds the earth and forms the spirit of man within him'.

On this account, the ancients believed that the earth had been made immobile, and, following Aristotle, they asserted that it was placed at the centre of the universe, where it was to be in its place of rest. But we say that it is not to be taken, as if He created an immobile world. And in support of this our belief we have, in the first place, Mathematics, in the second place, other passages of Scripture. What in heaven is more unfixed or mobile than the Moon? If, however, 'to found' signified 'to make immobile', David would be saying that it [the moon], along with the rest of the stars, was immobile, when he says: 'When I see Thy heavens, the works of Thy fingers, the moon and the stars which Thou hast founded'. In a similar way, God did not render the earth immobile, either by fixing or by establishing it, for Scripture attributes the same to heaven, as when David says: 'By the Word of the Lord were the heavens established, and by the Spirit of His mouth was all their strength (ordained)'. Likewise Solomon: 'The Lord by wisdom has founded the earth, by understanding He has established the heavens'.

Therefore, to us the passage quoted from Ps. 103 unties the entire knot of the discussion. Just as David said that the earth was founded,—that is, fixed and established—, on its foundations, which it is to keep for ever, so we also will correctly understand the Moon, and any other moving heavenly body, to be founded and fixed, as it were, on its stability, from which it will never decline. For it is clear that each of these bodies, by divine ordinance, is maintained in its 'way of being' (as we usually say).

For, although on earth there occur corruptions, generations, and all kinds of alterations, yet the earth itself remains in its wholeness as it was created. Fire, air, water, earth—everything keeps its place and fulfils the task for which it was created. Thus, as whatever Scripture means by the name 'earth', is founded on its own stability, so also are its parts, as the Psalmist bears witness when he says: 'Thou hast established the sea in Thy strengh', etc. But, whether there are changes in the Moon and the other heavenly bodies, or not, I do not see, how we could determine. For, if somebody would live on the Moon, I do not think that he would be able to judge anything about changes on earth. And Nicholas of Cusa, in his 'Learned Ignorance', argues at length that the earth also is luminous and so one of the stars. Furthermore, since motion also belongs to the way of being of the earth and of the other moving bodies, *it should be said that each of them has been founded on its stability, that is, so created, that it maintains its established course, (to use a term of Pliny's), and attains its prescribed positions.* And unless, for the sake of such a stability of motion, these things had been fixed in a definite and perpetual Law, we also would have no certain calculation of time, which God nevertheless wished us to have, as we read in the first chapter of Genesis. From all this it is plain that it cannot be proved from the sacred writings that the earth is immobile. Therefore, he who assumes its mobility in order to bring about a reliable calculation of times and motions, is not acting against Holy Scripture.

But let us come to the testimonies of Scripture concerning the Sun's mobility.

That the sun by its motion, assigned to it by God, is the originator of day and night and of all the changes of the seasons, and also is itself carried in an oblique circle, according to the hypotheses of Ptolemy and the ancients, seems to be proved by the following testimonies. *Genesis* 1: 'And God made two great lights, a greater light to rule the day and a lesser light to rule the night and the stars, and God placed them in the firmament of heaven, that they might shine upon the earth and rule the day and the night, and to divide the light from the darkness'. *Genesis* 19: 'The sun went out over the earth, and Lot went in to Zoar'.

Joshua, ch. 10: 12 *ff*: 'Then Joshua spoke to the Lord in the day in which He delivered up the Amorite in the sight of the children of Israel, and he said in their presence: Sun, do not move over Gibeon and Moon do not move over the valley of Ajalon. And the Sun and the Moon stood still until the people had avenged themselves upon their enemies', and then he adds: 'So the Sun stood still in the midst of heaven, and did not hasten to set for the space of one day. Never before and never since has there been so long a day, as when the Lord obeyed the voice of a man and fought for Israel'.

IV *Kings, ch.* 20, and *Isaiah, ch.* 38, addressing Hezekiah when he was ill: 'Behold, I shall cause the shadow of the lines through which it has gone down on the sundial of Ahaz to return ten lines. And the Sun went back ten lines, by which degrees it has gone down'.

Ecclesiasticus repeats this same passage in ch. 48, speaking about Hezekiah: 'In his days the Sun went back, and added life to the king'.

David, *Psalm* 103: 'He made the Moon for seasons. The Sun knows his setting'. The passage quoted from Genesis is repeated in *Psalm* 135 and in *Jeremiah, ch.* 37.

Baruch, ch. 6: 'The Sun also and the Moon and the stars obey, since they are magnificent and sent forth for their purposes'.

Ecclesiastes, ch. 1: 'The Sun rises and sets and returns to his place, whence rising again he revolves through the south and turns to the north. Illuminating the universe in his course the Spirit goes on and returns along his circles'.

So David in *Psalm* 18: 'He put His tabernacle in the Sun, who as a bridegroom coming from his wedding chamber rejoices like a giant to run the race; his coming forth is from the highest heaven. And his course is up till the highest [of it]; there is nothing which can hide from his heat'. To these testimonies of Scripture concerning the motion of the Sun, the answer is not difficult. We admit that the Sun is the natural source of light, and God's administrator, as the Psalmist says: 'He put His tabernacle in the Sun', in order to lighten the whole of created nature, and sends forth light and it goes, and He calls it back and it obeys Him in awe, as is written in *Baruch, ch. 3*.

Moreover, we do not deny obvious experience, which is that thanks to the Sun we have day, spring, summer and the other seasons of the year. But when we say that we receive these things from the Sun, just as the Moon receives its light, according to its changing relation to the Sun, we do so that it may be known to the learned through the authority of Urania, to whom the lover of truth must defer.—.

Furthermore, neither do we deny the clear words of Scripture,—since it does not assign a daily and a yearly motion to the Sun and, if you would have it so, also does not assign a motion of precession, since from it the seasons, days and years are measured as from a [fixed] point. Surely, we must consider what sort of movements these are. Everything that appears to move does so either because of the motion of the thing itself, or because of the movement of one's vision, or because of the movement of the object, as well as of the centre of vision. Common speech, however, mostly follows the judgment of the senses. Therefore these differences of movement are not distinguished in this from each other. This also, when a point of view determines something, and we know that in fact the matter stands otherwise, as it may often be noticed in everyday speech and in writings as, when following the judgment of our senses, while we sail from the harbour, we say that the land and the towns recede from us, and when navigating we say that the mountains and lands rise up out of the sea, and that the sun and the stars sink into it, and in our speech we do not distinguish the truth from the appearances.

When, however, we think as [persons] who seek the truth about things, we distinguish in our minds between appearance and reality. As the saying goes: we will judge as the few, but speak as the many. Thus when right reason concludes that the Sun is immobile, even though our eyes lead us to think it moves, we do not abandon the accepted way of speaking. We say that the Sun rises and sets, establishes the day and the year by its motion, even though we hold this to be true only in appearance, as our reason concludes to its immobility. In fact, it is the same going north, when we say that the pole [star] rises, because so it seems to us. But reason knows well that it stays fixed, and only seems to grow higher as we see it, because of our own moving towards it.

But it is too well-known to need further proof, that Holy Scripture uses common and received forms and figures of speech. Whence it is clear that, however much we insist on the many descriptions of the sun's movement adduced from

Scripture, these are to be understood as referring to its apparent motion, without in any way going beyond the bounds set by St. Augustine, nor introducing anything from which something inconvenient might follow. Therefore the texts of Scripture concerning the Sun's movement, which seem to argue against us, will not turn out to be at variance with the best verified results of the recent restoration of astronomy.

It is clear that, in these passages, we cannot keep to the letter, and accept the words and the letter in their proper meaning. Joshua orders the Sun not to move across Gibeon, and the Moon not to move across the valley of Ajalon. If Joshua had been in the city or on the other side of his army, it is certain that he would have seen these luminaries as though in other places, with respect to the earth. Therefore it is clear that he does not speak as a mathematician [astronomer] and that Scripture does not depart from ordinary speech. To illustrate this: Nicholas Perotti, a most learned man, talks in his 'Cornucopia' of the comet, which was seen in the year 1471, but overlooks this, when writing that he saw it above the house of Bessarion, and that it was the sign of his death. Perhaps it seemed like that from his house, but it is certain that from Bessarion's house he would have seen it somewhere else. In their explanation of the miracle of the prolonging of the day effected by God in the times of Joshua and Hezekiah, interpreters insist that nothing in the order or progress of the seasons was changed, and each tries to show this by different arguments. If, however, the motion of the earth is assumed, this is very easy to demonstrate. It was as when Israel crossed over the Jordan: the waters coming down from above, kept increasing in mass until, by God's concession, they resumed their course. The lower waters, however, flowed on, unhindered by their natural properties. So, though the earth ceased from its daily motion,—to those to whom the Sun was above the horizon, the day continued until God allowed it to return to its natural course,— nevertheless we say that the Moon held to its other apparent motions in relation to the earth and the Sun, and therefore nothing whatever in the year, nor in the month, nor in the celebration of the Passover was altered.

Habakkuk, ch. 3, where, in the Spirit, he foresees the destruction of Babylon by the Medes and the Persians, alludes to the story of Joshua, saying: 'The Sun and the Moon stood still in their dwelling', etc. This is interpreted that, just as the divine power was a help to Joshua, even so it brought assistance to the Medes and the Persians to occupy Babylon. Likewise, the Psalmist will be able to refer to this same story when, in *Psalm 75*, he predicts, in the Spirit, the destruction that was to be inflicted by the Angel on the Assyrians, saying: 'From heaven Thou hast caused the judgment to be heard, o God; the earth trembled and was still, when God arose in judgment, to save all the peaceful of the earth'. Though there is no mention in the story of the movement of the earth, if it is taken literally, it could be so understood, that, just as in the time of Joshua the earth, obeying the divine will in trembling, ceased from its daily motion when God fought for Israel,—so the Assyrians will fail when Thou removest their spirit from them and they are turned to dust, and for this Thy liberation from their enemies, the remnants give Thee thanks, etc. As far as I am concerned, anyone may interpret this passage figuratively, or in whatever way. What to the learned and pious has seemed the most suitable assumption in all this debate, we, too, shall follow.

As, however, everyone should in his calling, and by his talent, be of some service to the Catholic Church of Christ, the work of my lord preceptor should be examined (approved), which he gives to the Republic of Letters and which, under the guidance of mathematics, imparts to us a theory,—certain and in agreement with all ages—, of the seasons, years and days.

Finally, it also transmits an emended calculation of all the heavenly phenomena, whence, the way being pointed out by example, let us pursue, (in so far as God allows us), the knowledge of how the Lord also wished these most perfect bodies of the world to be known by us. The Philosophers say that some things are known to nature, but unknown to us. To this category let us indeed consign also disputes about hypotheses.For it appears that the Lord rightly said to Job: 'Hast thou known the order of heaven, and dost thou set up its plan on the earth?'

2.3 Christopher Marlowe, *The Tragedy of Dr. Faustus*, 1604, ll. 651–96, from Marlowe's *Works*

>*Faust.* I am resolv'd Faustus shall ne'er repent. 651
>Come, Mephistophilis, let us dispute again,
>And argue of divine astrology.
>Tell me, are there many heavens above the moon?
>Are all celestial bodies but one globe,
>As is the substance of this centric earth?
>   *Meph.* As are the elements, such are the spheres,
>Mutually folded in each other's orb,
>And, Faustus,
>All jointly move upon one axletree,   660
>Whose terminine is term'd the world's wide pole;
>Nor are the names of Saturn, Mars, or Jupiter
>Feign'd, but are erring stars.
>   *Faust.* But, tell me, have they all one motion, both
>*situ et tempore?*
>   *Meph.* All jointly move from east to west in twenty-
>four hours upon the poles of the world, but differ in
>their motion upon the poles of the zodiac.
>   *Faust.* Tush,
>These slender trifles Wagner can decide: 670
>Hath Mephistophilis no greater skill?
>Who knows not the double motion of the planets?
>The first is finish'd in a natural day;

The second thus; as Saturn in thirty years; Jupiter
in twelve; Mars in four; the Sun, Venus, and Mercury
in a year; the Moon in twenty-eight days. Tush, these
are freshmen's suppositions. But, tell me, hath every
sphere a dominion or *intelligentia*?

Meph. Ay.   679

Faust. How many heavens or spheres are there?

Meph. Nine; the seven planets, the firmament, and
the imperial heaven.

Faust. Well resolve me in this question; why have
we not conjunctions, oppositions, aspects, eclipses, all
at one time, but in some years we have more, in some
less?

Meph. Per inæqualem motum respectu totius.

Faust. Well, I am answered. Tell me who made the
world?

Meph. I will not

Faust. Sweet Mephistophilis, tell me.   690

Meph. Move me not, for I will not tell thee.

Faust. Villain, have I not bound thee to tell me
anything?

Meph. Ay, that is not against our kingdom; but this
is.

Think thou on hell, Faustus, for thou art damn'd.

Faust. Think, Faustus, upon God that made the
world.

Meph. Remember this.   [*Exit.*

Chapter 3: The spread of Copernicanism in northern Europe

3.1 Edward Wright, 'Laudatory address', in William Gilbert, *De Magnete*. London, 1600, pp. xxxvii–xlv

To the most learned Mr. William Gilbert, the distinguished London physician and father of the magnetic philosophy: a laudatory address concerning these books on magnetism, by Edward Wright.

Should there be any one, most worthy sir, who shall disparage these books and researches of yours, and who shall deem these studies trifling and in no wise sufficiently worthy of a man consecrated to the graver study of medicine, of a surety he will be esteemed no common simpleton. For that the uses of the loadstone are very considerable, yea admirable, is too well known even among men of the lowest class to call for many words from me at this time or for any commendation. In truth, in my opinion, there is no subject-matter of higher importance or of greater utility to the human race upon which you could have brought your philosophical talents to bear. For by the God-given favor of this stone has it come about that the things which for so many centuries lay hid— such vast continents of the globe, so infinite a number of countries, islands, nations and peoples—have been, almost within our own memory, easily discovered and oft explored, and that the whole circle of the globe has been circumnavigated more than once by our own Drake and Cavendish: which fact I wish to record for the undying remembrance of those men. For, by the showing of the magnetized needle, the points North, South, East and West and the other points of the compass are known to navigators, even while the sky is murky and in the deepest night; by this means seamen have understood toward what point they must steer their course, a thing that was quite impossible before the wondrous discovery of the north-pointing power of the loadstone. Hence sailors of old were often beset, as we learn from the histories, by an incredible anxiety and by great peril, for, when storms raged and the sight of sun and stars was cut off, they knew not whither they were sailing, neither could they by any means or by any device find out. Hence what must have been the gladness, what the joy of all mariners when first this magnetic pointer offered itself as a most sure guide on the route and as a God Mercury! But it was not enough for this magnetic Mercury simply to point out the way and, as it were, to show by the extended finger whither the course must be: it soon began even to indicate the distance of the place whither the voyage is made. For, since the magnetic pointer does not always regard the same northern spot in every locality, but usually varies therefrom, either to the east or to the west, tho' it nevertheless hath and holds ever the same variation in the same place, wherever that may be; it has come about that by means of this variation (as it is called) closely observed and noted in certain maritime regions, together with an

18

observation of the latitude, the same places can afterward be found by navigators when they approach and come near to the same variation. Herein the Portuguese in their voyages to the East Indies have the surest tokens of their approaching the Cape of Good Hope, as is shown in the narrations of Hugo *Lynschetensis* and our very learned fellow-countryman Richard Hakluyt; hereby, too, many of our skilled British navigators when voyaging from the Gulf of Mexico to the Azores, can tell when they are come near to these islands, though, according to their marine charts, they may appear to be 600 English miles away. And thus, thanks to this magnetic indication, that ancient geographical problem, how to discover the longitude, would seem to be on the way to a solution; for, the variation of a seaboard place being known, that place can thereafter be very easily found as often as occasion may require, provided its latitude is not unknown.

Yet somewhat of inconvenience and difficulty seems to attach to this observation of the variation, for it cannot be made except when the sun or the stars are shining. Accordingly this magnetic Mercury of the sea, better far than Neptune himself or any of the sea gods or goddesses, proceeds still further to bestow blessings on all mariners; and not alone in the darkness of night and when the sky is murky does he show the true direction, but he seems even to give the surest indications of the latitude. For the iron pointer suspended freely and with the utmost precision in equilibrium on its axis, and then touched and excited with a loadstone, dips down to a fixed and definite point below the horizon (e.g. in the latitude of London it dips nearly 72 degrees) and there stands. But because of the wonderful agreement and congruency manifested in nearly all and singular magnetic experiments, equally in the earth itself and in a terrella (i.e. a spherical loadstone), it seems (to say the least) highly probable and more than probable that the same pointer (similarly stroked with a loadstone) will, at the equator, stand in equilibrium on the plane of the horizon. Hence, too, it is highly probable that in proceeding a very short distance from south to north (or *vice versa*) there will be a pretty sensible change in the dip; and thus the dip being carefully noted once and the latitude observed, the same place and the same latitude may thereafter be very readily found by means of a dip instrument even in the darkest night and in the thickest weather.

Thus then, to bring our discourse back again to you, most worthy and learned Mr. Gilbert (whom I gladly acknowledge as my master in this magnetical philosophy), if these books of yours on the Loadstone contained nought save this one method of finding the latitude from the magnetic dip, now first published by you, even so our British mariners as well as the French, the Dutch, the Danes, whenever they have to enter the British sea or the strait of Gibraltar from the Atlantic Ocean, will justly hold them worth no small sum of gold. And that discovery of yours, that the entire globe is magnetical, albeit to many it will seem to the last degree paradoxical, nevertheless is buttressed and confirmed by so many and so apposite experiments in Book II, Chapter XXXIV; Book III, Chapters IV and XII; and throughout nearly the whole of Book V, that no room is left for doubt or contradiction. I come therefore to the cause of magnetic variation—a problem that till now has perplexed the minds of the learned; but no one ever set forth a cause more probable than the one proposed now for the first time in these your books on the Loadstone. The fact that the magnetic needle points due north in the middle of the ocean and in the heart of continents—or at least in the heart of their more massive and more elevated parts—while near the coasts there is, afloat and ashore, an inclination of the needle toward those more massive parts, just as happens in a terrella that is made to resemble the earth globe in its greater elevation at some parts and shows that it is weak or decayed or otherwise imperfect elsewhere: all this makes exceedingly probable the theory that the variation is nothing but a deviation of the magnetic needle to those more powerful and more elevated regions of the globe. Hence the reason of the irregularity that is seen in the variations of the compass is easily found in the inequality and anomaly of those more elevated parts. Nor do I doubt that all those who have imagined or accepted certain 'respective points' as well as they who speak of magnetic mountains or rocks or poles, will begin to waver as soon as they read these your books on the Loadstone and will of their own accord come over to your opinion.

As for what you have finally to say of the circular motion of the earth and the terrestrial poles, though many will deem it the merest theorizing, still I do not see why it should not meet with indulgence even among those who do not acknowledge the earth's motion to be spherical, seeing that even they cannot readily extricate themselves from the many difficulties that result from a diurnal motion of the whole heavens. For, first, it is not reasonable to have that done by many agents which can be done by fewer, or to have the whole heavens and all the spheres (if spheres there be) of the planets and fixed stars made to revolve for the sake of the diurnal motion, which may be accounted for by a daily rotation of the earth. Then, which theory is the more probable, that the equinoctial circle of the earth may make a rotatary movement of one quarter of an English mile (60 miles being equal to one degree on the earth's equator) in one second of time, i.e., in about as much time as it takes to make only one step when one is walking rapidly; or that the equator of the *primum mobile* in the same time, with inexpressible celerity, makes 5000 miles and that in the twinkling of an eye it makes about 50 English miles, surpassing the velocity of a flash of lightning, if they are in the right who most strenuously deny the earth's motion? Finally, which is the more probable, to suppose that this little globe of the earth has some motion, or with mad license of conjecture to superpose three mighty starless spheres, a ninth, a tenth, and an eleventh, upon the eighth sphere of the fixed stars, particularly when from these books on the Loadstone and the comparison of the earth with the terrella it is plain that spherical motion is not so contrary to the nature of the earth as it is commonly supposed to be?

Nor do the passages quoted from Holy Writ appear to contradict very strongly the doctrine of the earth's mobility. It does not seem to have been the intention of Moses or the prophets to promulgate nice mathematical or physical distinctions: they rather adapt themselves to the understanding of the common people and to the current fashion of speech, as nurses do in dealing with babes; they do not attend to unessential minutiæ. Thus, Genesis i. 16 and Psalm cxxxvi. 7, 9, the moon is called a great luminary, because it so appears to us, though, to those versed in astronomy, it is known that very many stars, fixed and planetary, are far larger. So, too, from Ps. civ. 5, no argument of any weight can, I think, be drawn to contradict the earth's mobility, albeit it is said that God established the earth on her foundations to the end it should never be moved; for the earth may remain forevermore in its own place and in the selfsame place, in such manner that it shall not be moved away by any stray force of transference, nor carried beyond its abiding place wherein it was established in the beginning by the divine architect. We, therefore, while we devoutly acknowledge and adore the inscrutable wisdom of the triune Godhead, having with all diligence investigated and discerned the wondrous work of his hands in the magnetic movements, do hold it to be entirely probable, on the ground of experiments and philosophical reasons not few, that the earth while it rests on its centre as its basis and foundation, hath a spherical motion nevertheless.

But, apart from these matters (touching which no one, I do believe, ever gave more certain demonstrations), no doubt your discussion of the causes of variation and of the dip of the needle beneath the horizon (to say nothing of sundry other points which 'twould take too long to mention) will find the heartiest approval among all intelligent men and 'children, of magnetic science' (to use the language of the chemists). Nor have I any doubt that, by publishing these your books on the Loadstone, you will stimulate all wide-awake navigators to give not less study to observation of dip than of variation. For it is highly probable, if not certain, that latitude, or rather the effect of latitude, can be determined much more accurately (even when the sky is darkest) from the dip alone, than longitude or the effect of longitude can be found from the variation even in the full light of day or while all the stars are shining, and with the help of the most skilfully and ingeniously contrived instrument. Nor is there any doubt that those most learned men, Petrus Plantius (a most diligent student not so much of geography as of magnetic observations) and Simon Stevinius, a most eminent mathematician, will be not a little rejoiced when first they set eyes on these your books and therein see their own λιμνευρετικήν or method of finding ports so greatly and unexpectedly enlarged and developed; and of course they will, as far as they may be able, induce all navigators among their own countrymen to note the dip no less than the variation of the needle.

Let your magnetic Philosophy, most learned Mr. Gilbert, go forth then under the best auspices—that work held back not for nine years only, according to Horace's Counsel, but for almost other nine; that Philosophy which by your multitudinous labors, studies, vigils, and by your skill and at your no inconsiderable expense has been after long years at last, by means of countless ingenious experiments, taken bodily out of the darkness and dense murkiness with which it was surrounded by the speculations of incompetent and shallow philosophizers; nor did you in the mean time overlook, but did diligently read and digest whatever had been published in the writings whether of the ancients or the moderns. Let it not be afraid to face the prejudiced censure of any supercilious and dastardly philosophaster who, by enviously faulting another's work or by fraudulently taking the credit to himself, strives to win a most unsubstantial renown; for

Ingenium magni livor detrectat Homeri,
(Envy detracts from the genius of mighty Homer):

but

Quisquis es, ex illo, Zoile, nomen habes.
(whoever thou art, from him, Zoilus, dost thou derive thy fame.)

Your work, I say, that has been kept back for so many years, your New Physiology of the Loadstone and of the Great Magnet (i.e. the Earth)—a philosophy never to be sufficiently admired; let it go forth into the light of publicity; for, believe me,

Siquid habent veri vatum præsagia,
(If the presages of poets have aught of truth)

these your books on the Loadstone (*De Magnete*) will do more to perpetuate your memory than would the monument of any Magnate (*Magnatis cujusvis*) erected over your grave.

3.2 J. Kepler, *Astronomia Nova*, Heidelberg, 1609; trans. C. A. Russell, from D. C. Goodman (ed.), *Science and Religious Belief 1600–1900*, 1973, pp. 22–3. Wright/Open University Press, Bristol

See Chapter 10 of my *Astronomy: the Optical Section* where you will find reasons why the sun in this way seems to all men to be moving, but not the earth: namely, because the sun seems small, but the earth truly appears to be large. Nor is the motion of the sun to be grasped by sight (since it gives the appearance of being slow) but by reason alone on account of the changed relationship to the mountains after some time. It is therefore impossible that reason not previously instructed should imagine anything other than that the earth is a kind of vast house with the vault of the sky placed on top of it; it is motionless and within it the sun being so small passes from one region to another, like a bird wandering through the air.

This universal image has produced the first line in the sacred page. *In the beginning,* said Moses, *God created the heaven and the earth;* this is a natural expression because these two aspects of the universe are those that chiefly meet the eye. It is as if Moses were saying to man 'all this architecture of the universe that you see, the brightness above, by which you are covered, the widespreading darkness below, upon which you stand—all this had been created by God'.

In other places man is questioned whether he has learned how to penetrate the height of the sky above or the depth of the earth beneath. This is natural because to the mass of men each of these appears equally to project into infinite space. Nevertheless, there never was a man who, listening rationally, would use these words to circumscribe the diligence of the astronomers, whether in demonstrating the most contemptible weakness of the earth by comparison with the sky, or through investigations of astronomical distance. These words do not speak about intellectualised dimensions, but about the dimension of reality—which, for a human body fixed on the earth and drinking in the free air, is totally impossible. Read the whole of Job Ch. 38 and compare with it the matters that are disputed in astronomy and physics.

If anyone alleges on the basis of Psalm 24 *The earth is founded upon the seas* (in order to establish some new philosophical dictum, however absurd to hear) that the earth is floating on the waters, may it not be rightly said to him that he ought to set free the Holy Spirit and should not drag Him in to the schools of physics to make a fool of Him. For in that place the Psalmist wishes to suggest nothing other than what men know beforehand and experience each day: the lands, uplifted after separation of the waters, have great rivers flowing through them and the seas around them on all sides. Doubtless the same is spoken of elsewhere, when the Israelites sing *By the waters of Babylon there we sat down*, i.e., by the side of the rivers, or on the banks of the Euphrates and Tigris.

If anyone receives the one freely, why not the other, so that in other places which are often quoted against the motion of the earth we should, in the same way, turn our eyes from physics to the tradition of scripture?

One generation passes away, says Ecclesiastes, *and another generation is born*, but the earth abides for ever. Is Solomon here, as it were, disputing with the astronomers? No, he is rather warning men of their changeableness whereas the earth, the home of the human race, always remains the same; the movement of the sun keeps returning it to its starting-point; the wind is driven in a circle, and returns to the same plan; rivers flow from their sources to the sea, and thence return to their sources. Finally, while some men perish others are born, and always the drama of life is the same; there is nothing new under the sun.

You are listening to no new principle of physics. It is a question of ethical instruction in a matter which is clear on its own, observed universally but receives scant consideration. That is why Solomon insists on the matter. Who does not know the earth to be always the same? Who does not see that the sun rising daily in the East, that the rivers run perpetually down to the sea, that the pattern of changes of the wind is fixed and recurring and that one generation succeeds another? Who in fact considers that the drama of life is being perpetually performed, with only a change of cast and that there is nothing new in human affairs? And so, by rehearsing things which everyone sees, Solomon warns of that which the majority wrongly neglect.

But some men think Psalm 104 to be wholly concerned with physics, since it is wholly concerned with physical matters. And there God is said to have *laid the foundations of the earth so that it should not be moved,* and that stability will remain from age to age. Nevertheless the Psalmist is a very long way from speculation about physical causes. He rests utterly in the greatness of God who made all these things and is unfolding a hymn to God the Creator, a hymn in which he runs in order through the whole world as it appears to our eyes.

3.3 John Donne, 'First Anniversarie', 1611, ll. 205–14, 251–82, from Donne's *Works*

And new Philosophy calls all in doubt,   205
The Element of fire is quite put out;
The Sun is lost, and th'earth, and no mans wit
Can well direct him where to looke for it.
And freely men confesse that this world's spent,
When in the Planets, and the Firmament   210
They seeke so many new; they see that this
Is crumbled out againe to his Atomies.
'Tis all in peeces, all cohaerence gone;
All just supply, and all Relation:

. . .

We thinke the heavens enjoy their Sphericall,
Their round proportion embracing all.
But yet their various and perplexed course,
Observ'd in divers ages, doth enforce
Men to finde out so many Eccentrique parts,   255
Such divers downe-right lines, such overthwarts,
As disproportion that pure forme: It teares
The Firmament in eight and forty sheires,
And in these Constellations then arise
New starres, and old doe vanish from our eyes: 260
As though heav'n suffered earthquakes, peace or war,
When new Towers rise, and old demolish't are.
They have impal'd within a Zodiake
The free-borne Sun, and keepe twelve Signes awake
To watch his steps; the Goat and Crab controule,   265
And fright him backe, who else to either Pole
(Did not these Tropiques fetter him) might runne:
For his course is not round; nor can the Sunne
Perfit a Circle, or maintaine his way
One inch direct; but where he rose to-day   270
He comes no more, but with a couzening line,
Steales by that point, and so is Serpentine:
And seeming weary with his reeling thus,
He meanes to sleepe, being now falne nearer us.

So, of the Starres which boast that they doe runne   275
In Circle still, none ends where he begun.
All their proportion's lame, it sinkes, it swels.
For of Meridians, and Parallels,
Man hath weav'd out a net, and this net throwne
Upon the Heavens, and now they are his owne.   280
Loth to goe up the hill, or labour thus
To goe to heaven, we make heaven come to us.

3.4 John Wilkins, *A Discourse concerning a New Planet*, London, 1640, Book 2, pp. 8–13

In weighing the Authority of others, 'tis not their multitude   LIB. 2. *Confid.* 2. *Cap.* 1.
that should prevaile, or their skill in some things that should
make them of credit in everything, but wee should examine
what particular insight and experience they had in those
times for which they are cited. Now 'tis plaine, that common
people judge by their senses; and therefore, their voices are
altogether unfit to decide any Philosophicall doubt, which
cannot well be examined or explained without discourse and
reason. And as the for antient Fathers, though they were
men very eminent for their holy lives and extraordinary skill
in Divinitie; yet they were most of them very ignorant in
that part of Learning which concernes this opinion, as
appeares by many of their grosse mistakes in this kinde, as
that concerning the *Antipodes*, &c. and therefore it is not
their opinion neither, in this businesse, that to an indifferent
seeker of Truth will bee of any strong Authority.

But against this it is *objected, That the instance of the   *Alex. Ross. l. 1.
Antipodes do's not argue any speciall ignorance in these   sect. c. 8.
learned men: Or, that they had lesse skil in such humane   LIB. 2. *Cap.* 1.
Arts than others; since *Aristotle* himself, and *Pliny*, did deny
this as well as they.

I answer:

1   If they did, yet this do's make more to the present
purpose: For if such great Schollers, who were so eminent
for their knowledge in naturall things, might yet notwithstanding be grossely mistaken in such matters as are now
evident and certaine: Why thenwee have no reason to
depend upon their assertions or Authorities, as if they were
infallible.

2   Though these great Naturalists, for want of some experience were mistaken in that opinion, whilest they thought
no place was habitable but the temperate *Zones*; yet it cannot
be from hence inferred, that they denied the possibilitie of
Antipodes: since these are such Inhabitants as live opposite
unto us in the other temperate *Zone*; and 'twere an absurd
thing to imagine that those who lived in different *Zones*, can
be *Antipodes* to one another; and argues that a man did not
understand, or else had forgotton that common distinction
in *Geography*, wherein the relation of the Worlds Inhabitants
unto one another, are reckoned up under these three heads;
Antæci, Periæci, and *Antipodes.* But to let this passe: 'Tis certaine,
that some of the Fathers did deny the being of any such,
upon other more absurd grounds. Now if such as *Chrisostome,
Lactantius,* &c. who were noted for great Schollers, and such
too as flourished in these latter times, when all humane
Learning was more generally profest, should notwithstanding
be so much mistaken in so obvious a matter: Why then may
wee not think that those Primitive Saints, who were the
pen-men of Scripture, and eminent above others in their time
for holinesse and knowledge, might yet be utterly ignorant
of many Philosophicall Truths, which are commonly knowne
in these dayes? 'Tis probable, that the Holy Ghost did
informe them onely with the knowledge of those things
whereof they were to be the pen-men, and that they were
not better skilled in points of Philosophy than others. There
were indeed some of them who were supernaturally indowed
with humane Learning; yet this was, because they might
thereby bee fitted for some particular ends, which all the
rest were not appointed unto: thus *Solomon* was strangely
gifted with all kinde of knowledge, in a great measure,
because he was to teach us by his owne experience the

Eccl. 1.18.   extreme vanity of it, that we might not so settle our desires
upon it, as if it were able to yeeld us contentment. So too
the Apostles were extraordinarily inspired with the knowledge of Languages, because they were to preache unto all
Nations. But it will not hence follow, that therfore the other
holy pen-men were greater Schollers than others. 'Tis likely
that *Iob* had as much humane Learning as most of them,
because his Booke is more especially remarkable for lofty
expressions, and discourses of Nature; and yet 'tis not likely
that he was acquainted with all those mysteries which later
Ages have discovered; because when God would convince
him of his owne folly and ignorance, he proposes to him
such questions, as being altogether unanswerable; which
notwithstanding,   any   ordinary   Philosopher   in   these

dayes might have resolued. As you may see at large in the
thirty eighth Chapter of that Booke.
Lɪʙ. 2. *Cap.* 1.

The occasion was this: *Iob* having *before desired that he
might dispute with the Almighty concerning the uprightnesse
of his own wayes, and the unreasonablenesse of those
afflictions which he underwent, do's at length obtaine his
desire in this kind; and God vouchsafes in this thirty eighth
chapter, to argue the case with him. Where he do's shew
Iob how unfit he was to judge of the wayes of Providence,
in disposing of Blessings and Afflictions, when as he was so
ignorant in ordinary matters, being not able to discerne the
reason of naturall and common events. As *why the Sea
should bee so bounded from overflowing the land? What is
the †bredth of the Earth? what is the *reason of the Snow
or Hayle? what was the ‡cause of the Raine or Dewe, of
Ice and Frost, and the like. By which questions, it seemes
Iob was so utterly pusled, thathee is faine afterwards to
humble himselfe in this acknowledgement: §*I have uttered
that I understood not, things too wonderfull for me, which I knew
not: wherefore I abhorre my selfe, and repent in dust and ashes.*

Cap. 13.3.

*V. 8.10, 11.

†Ver. 18.
*Ver. 22.
‡V. 28.29.

§*Cap.* 42.3

3.5 J. Kepler, *Harmonices Mundi*, 1619; trans. C. G. Wallis, from *Great Books of the World*, vol. 16, 1952, pp. 1014–18, 1040–1. Chicago: Encyclopaedia Britannica Inc.

3. A Summary of Astronomical Doctrine Necessary for Speculation into the Celestial Harmonies

First of all, my readers should know that the ancient astronomical hypotheses
of Ptolemy, in the fashion in which they have been unfolded in the *Theoricae* of
Peurbach and by the other writers of epitomes, are to be completely removed
from this discussion and cast out of the mind. For they do not convey the true
lay out of the bodies of the world and the polity of the movements.

Although I cannot do otherwise than to put solely Copernicus' opinion
concerning the world in the place of those hypotheses and, if that were possible,
to persuade everyone of it; but because the thing is still new among the mass
of the intelligentsia [*apud vulgus studiosorum*], and the doctrine that the Earth is
one of the planets and moves among the stars around a motionless sun sounds
very absurd to the ears of most of them: therefore those who are shocked by
the unfamiliarity of this opinion should know that these harmonical speculations
are possible even with the hypotheses of Tycho Brahe—because that author
holds, in common with Copernicus, everything else which pertains to the lay
out of the bodies and the tempering of the movements, and transfers solely the

Copernican annual movement of the Earth to the whole system of planetary spheres and to the sun, which occupies the centre of that system, in the opinion of both authors. For after this transference of movement it is nevertheless true that in Brahe the Earth occupies at any time the same place that Copernicus gives it, if not in the very vast and measureless region of the fixed stars, at least in the system of the planetary world. And accordingly, just as he who draws a circle on paper makes the writing-foot of the compass revolve, while he who fastens the paper or tablet to a turning lathe draws the same circle on the revolving tablet with the foot of the compass or stylus motionless; so too, in the case of Copernicus the Earth, by the real movement of its body, measures out a circle revolving midway between the circle of Mars on the outside and that of Venus on the inside; but in the case of Tycho Brahe the whole planetary system (wherein among the rest the circles of Mars and Venus are found) revolves like a tablet on a lathe and applies to the motionless Earth, or to the stylus on the lathe, the midspace between the circles of Mars and Venus; and it comes about from this movement of the system that the Earth within it, although remaining motionless, marks out the same circle around the sun and midway between Mars and Venus, which in Copernicus it marks out by the real movement of its body while the system is at rest. Therefore, since harmonic speculation considers the eccentric movements of the planets, as if seen from the sun, you may easily understand that if any observer were stationed on a sun as much in motion as you please, nevertheless for him the Earth, although at rest (as a concession to Brahe), would seem to describe the annual circle midway between the planets and in an intermediate length of time. Wherefore, if there is any man of such feeble wit that he cannot grasp the movement of the earth among the stars, nevertheless he can take pleasure in the most excellent spectacle of this most divine construction, if he applies to their image in the sun whatever he hears concerning the daily movements of the Earth in its eccentric—such an image as Tycho Brahe exhibits, with the Earth at rest.

And nevertheless the followers of the true Samian philosophy have no just cause to be jealous of sharing this delightful speculation with such persons, because their joy will be in many ways more perfect, as due to the consummate perfection of speculation, if they have accepted the immobility of the sun and the movement of the earth.

Firstly [I], therefore, let my readers grasp that today it is absolutely certain among all astronomers that all the planets revolve around the sun, with the exception of the moon, which alone has the Earth as its centre: the magnitude of the moon's sphere or orbit is not great enough for it to be delineated in this diagram in a just ratio to the rest. Therefore, to the other five planets, a sixth, the Earth, is added, which traces a sixth circle around the sun, whether by its own proper movement with the sun at rest, or motionless itself and with the whole planetary system revolving.

Secondly [II]: It is also certain that all the planets are eccentric, i.e, they change their distances from the sun, in such fashion that in one part of their circle they become farthest away from the sun, [276] and in the opposite part they come

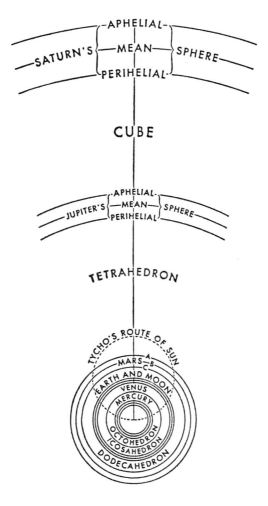

nearest to the sun. In the accompanying diagram three circles apiece have been drawn for the single planets: none of them indicate the eccentric route of the planet itself; but the mean circle, such as *BE* in the case of Mars, is equal to the eccentric orbit, with respect to its longer diameter. But the orbit itself, such as *AD*, touches *AF*, the upper of the three, in one place *A*, and the lower circle *CD*, in the opposite place *D*. The circle *GH* made with dots and described through the centre of the sun indicates the route of the sun according to Tycho Brahe. And if the sun moves on this route, then absolutely all the points in this whole planetary system here depicted advance upon an equal route, each upon his own. And with one point of it (namely, the centre of the sun) stationed at one point of its circle, as here at the lowest, absolutely each and every point of the system will be stationed at the lowest part of its circle. However, on account of the smallness of the space the three circles of Venus unite in one, contrary to my intention.

Thirdly [III]: Let the reader recall from my *Mysterium Cosmographicum*, which I published twenty-two years ago, that the number of the planets or circular routes around the sun was taken by the very wise Founder from the five regular solids, concerning which Euclid, so many ages ago, wrote his book which is called the *Elements* in that it is built up out of a series of propositions. But it has been made clear in the second book of this work that there cannot be more regular bodies, *i.e.*, that regular plane figures cannot fit together in a solid more than five times.

Fourthly [IV]: As regards the ratio of the planetary orbits, the ratio between two neighbouring planetary orbits is always of such a magnitude that it is easily apparent that each and every one of them approaches the single ratio of the spheres of one of the five regular solids, namely, that of the sphere circumscribing to the sphere inscribed in the figure. Nevertheless it is not wholly equal, as I once dared to promise concerning the final perfection of astronomy. For, after completing the demonstration of the intervals from Brahe's observations, I discovered the following: if the angles of the cube are applied to the inmost circle of Saturn, the centres of the planes are approximately tangent to the middle circle of Jupiter; and if the angles of the tetrahedron are placed against the inmost circle of Jupiter, the centres of the planes of the tetrahedron are approximately tangent to the outmost circle of Mars; thus if the angles of the octahedron are placed against any circle of Venus (for the total interval between the three has been very much reduced), the centres of the planes of the octahedron penetrate and descend deeply within the outmost circle of Mercury, but nonetheless do not reach as far as the middle circle of Mercury; and finally, closest of all to the ratios of the dodecahedral and icosahedral spheres—which ratios are equal to one another—are the ratios or intervals between the circles of Mars and the Earth, and the Earth and Venus; and those intervals are similarly equal, if we compute from the inmost circle of Mars to the middle circle of the Earth, but from the middle circle of the Earth to the middle circle of Venus. For the middle distance of the Earth is a mean proportional between the least distance of Mars and the middle distance of Venus. However, these two ratios between the planetary circles are still greater than the ratios of those two pairs of spheres in the figures, in such fashion that the centres of the dodecahedral planes are not tangent to the outmost circle of the Earth, and the centres of the icosahedral planes are not tangent to the outmost circle of Venus; nor, however, can this gap be filled by the semidiameter of the lunar sphere, by adding it, on the upper side, to the greatest distance of the Earth and subtracting it, on the lower, from the least distance of the same. But I find a certain other ratio of figures—namely, if I take the augmented dodecahedron, to which I have given the name of echinus, (as being fashioned from twelve quinquangular stars and thereby very close to the five regular solids), if I take it, I say, and place its twelve points in the inmost circle of Mars, then the sides of the pentagons, which are the bases of the single rays or points, touch the middle circle of Venus. In short: the cube and the octahedron, which are consorts, do not penetrate their planetary spheres at all; the dodecahedron and the icosahedron, which are consorts, do not wholly reach to theirs, the tetrahedron exactly touches both: in the first case there is falling short; in the second, excess; and in the third, equality, with respect to the planetary intervals.

Wherefore it is clear that the very ratios of the planetary intervals from the sun have not been taken from the regular solids alone. For the Creator, who is the very source of geometry and, as Plato wrote, 'practices eternal geometry,' does not stray from his own archetype. And indeed that very thing could be inferred from the fact that all the planets change their intervals throughout fixed periods of time, in such fashion that each has two marked intervals from the sun, a greatest and a least; and a fourfold comparison of the intervals from the sun is possible between two planets: the comparison can be made between either the greatest, or the least, or the contrary intervals most remote from one another, or the contrary intervals nearest together. In this way the comparisons made two by two between neighbouring planets are twenty in number, although on the contrary there are only five regular solids. But it is consonant that if the Creator had any concern for the ratio of the spheres in general, He would also have had concern for the ratio which exists between the varying intervals of the single planets specifically and that the concern is the same in both cases and the one is bound up with the other. If we ponder that, we will comprehend that for setting up the diameters and eccentricities conjointly, there is need of more principles, outside of the five regular solids. [. . .]

7. The Universal Consonances of All Six Planets, Like Common Four-Part Counterpoint, Can Exist

But now, Urania, there is need for louder sound while I climb along the harmonic scale of the celestial movements to higher things where the true archetype of the fabric of the world is kept hidden. Follow after, ye modern musicians, and judge the thing according to your arts, which were unknown to antiquity. Nature, which is never not lavish of herself, after a lying-in of two thousand years, has finally brought you forth in these last generations, the first true images of the universe. By means of your concords of various voices, and through your ears, she has whispered to the human mind, the favorite daughter of God the Creator, how she exists in the innermost bosom.

(Shall I have committed a crime if I ask the single composers of this generation for some artistic motet instead of this epigraph? The Royal Psalter and the other Holy Books can supply a text suited for this. But alas for you! No more than six are in concord in the heavens. For the moon sings here monody separately, like a dog sitting on the Earth. Compose the melody; I, in order that the book may progress, promise that I will watch carefully over the six parts. To him who more properly expresses the celestial music described in this work, Clio will give a garland, and Urania will betroth Venus his bride.)

It has been unfolded above what harmonic ratios two neighbouring planets would embrace in their extreme movements. But it happens very rarely that two, especially the slowest, arrive at their extreme intervals at the same time;

For example, the apsides of Saturn and Jupiter are about 81° apart. Accordingly, while this distance between them measures out the whole zodiac by definite twenty-year leaps, eight hundred years pass by, and nonetheless the leap which concludes the eighth century, does not carry precisely to the very apsides; and if it digresses much further, another eight hundred years must be awaited, that a more fortunate leap than that one may be sought; and the whole route must be repeated as many times as the measure of digression is contained in the length of one leap. Moreover, the other single pairs of planets have periods like that, although not so long. But meanwhile there occur also other consonances of two planets, between movements whereof not both are extremes but one or both are intermediate; and those consonances exist as it were in different tunings [*tensionibus*]. For, because Saturn tends from G to b, and slightly further, and Jupiter from b to d and further; therefore between Jupiter and Saturn there can exist the following consonances, over and above the octave: the major and minor third and the perfect fourth, either one of the thirds through the tuning which maintains the amplitude of the remaining one, but the perfect fourth through the amplitude of a major whole tone. For there will be a perfect fourth not merely from G of Saturn to cc of Jupiter but also from A of Saturn to dd of Jupiter and through all the intermediates between the G and A of Saturn and the cc and dd of Jupiter. But the octave and the perfect fifth exist solely at the points of the apsides. But Mars, which got a greater interval as its own, received it in order that it should also make an octave with the upper planets through some amplitude of tuning. Mercury received an interval great enough for it to set up almost all the consonances with all the planets within one of its periods, which is not longer than the space of three months. On the other hand, the Earth, and Venus much more so, on account of the smallness of their intervals, limit the consonances, which they form not merely with the others but with one another in especial, to visible fewness. But if three planets are to concord in one harmony, many periodic returns are to be awaited; nevertheless there are many consonances, so that they may so much the more easily take place, while each nearest consonance follows after its neighbour, and very often threefold consonances are seen to exist between Mars, the Earth, and Mercury. But the consonances of four planets now begin to be scattered throughout centuries, and those of five planets throughout thousands of years.

But that all six should be in concord has been fenced about by the longest intervals of time; and I do not know whether it is absolutely impossible for this to occur twice by precise evolving or whether that points to a certain beginning of time, from which every age of the world has flowed.

But if only one sextuple harmony can occur, or only one notable one among many, indubitably that could be taken as a sign of the Creation. Therefore we must ask, in exactly how many forms are the movements of all six planets reduced to one common harmony? The method of inquiry is as follows: let us begin with the Earth and Venus, because these two planets do not make more than two consonances and (wherein the cause of this thing is comprehended) by means of very short intensifications of the movements.

Chapter 4: Crisis in Italy

4.1 Letter from Galileo to Grand Duchess Christina, 1615; trans. Stillman Drake, from *Discoveries and Opinions of Galileo*, 1957, extracts from pp. 181–200. New York: Doubleday

The reason produced for condemning the opinion that the earth moves and the sun stands still is that in many places in the Bible one may read that the sun moves and the earth stands still. Since the Bible cannot err, it follows as a necessary consequence that anyone takes an erroneous and heretical position who maintains that the sun is inherently motionless and the earth movable.

With regard to this argument, I think in the first place that it is very pious to say and prudent to affirm that the holy Bible can never speak untruth—whenever its true meaning is understood. But I believe nobody will deny that it is often very abstruse, and may say things which are quite different from what its bare words signify. Hence in expounding the Bible if one were always to confine oneself to the unadorned grammatical meaning, one might fall into error. Not only contradictions and propositions far from true might thus be made to appear in the Bible, but even grave heresies and follies. Thus it would be necessary to assign to God feet, hands, and eyes, as well as corporeal and human affections, such as anger, repentance, hatred, and sometimes even the forgetting of things past and ignorance of those to come. These propositions uttered by the Holy Ghost were set down in that manner by the sacred scribes in order to accommodate them to the capacities of the common people, who are rude and unlearned. For the sake of those who deserve to be separated from the herd, it is necessary that wise expositors should produce the true senses of such passages, together with the special reasons for which they were set down in these words. This doctrine is so widespread and so definite with all theologians that it would be superfluous to adduce evidence for it.

Hence I think that I may reasonably conclude that whenever the Bible has occasion to speak of any physical conclusion (especially those which are very abtruse and hard to understand), the rule has been observed of avoiding confusion in the minds of the common people which would render them contumacious toward the higher mysteries. Now the Bible, merely to condescend to popular capacity, has not hesitated to obscure some very important pronouncements, attributing to God himself some qualities extremely remote from (and even contrary to) His essence. Who, then, would positively declare that this principle has been set aside, and the Bible has confined itself rigorously to the bare and restricted sense of its words, when speaking but casually of the earth, of water, of the sun, or of any other created thing? Especially in view of the fact that these things in no way concern the primary purpose of the sacred writings, which is the service of God and the salvation of souls—matters infinitely beyond the comprehension of the common people.

This being granted, I think that in discussions of physical problems we ought to begin not from the authority of scriptural passages, but from sense-experiences and necessary demonstrations; for the holy Bible and the phenomena of nature proceed alike from the divine Word, the former as the dictate of the Holy Ghost and the latter as the observant executrix of God's commands. It is necessary for the Bible, in order to be accommodated to the understanding of every man, to speak many things which appear to differ from the absolute truth so far as the bare meaning of the words is concerned. But Nature, on the other hand, is inexorable and immutable; she never transgresses the laws imposed upon her, or cares a whit whether her abstruse reasons and methods of operation are understandable to men. For that reason it appears that nothing physical which sense-experience sets before our eyes, or which necessary demonstrations prove to us, ought to be called in question (much less condemned) upon the testimony of biblical passages which may have some different meaning beneath their words. For the Bible is not chained in every expression to conditions as strict as those which govern all physical effects; nor is God any less excellently revealed in Nature's actions than in the sacred statements of the Bible. [. . .]

But I do not feel obliged to believe that that same God who has endowed us with senses, reason, and intellect has intended to forgo their use and by some other means to give us knowledge which we can attain by them. He would not require us to deny sense and reason in physical matters which are set before our eyes and minds by direct experience or necessary demonstrations. This must be especially true in those sciences of which but the faintest trace (and that consisting of conclusions) is to be found in the Bible. Of astronomy, for instance, so little is found that none of the planets except Venus are so much as mentioned, and this only once or twice under the name of 'Lucifer'. If the sacred scribes had had any intention of teaching people certain arrangements and motions of the heavenly bodies, or had they wished us to derive such knowledge from the Bible, then in my opinion they would not have spoken of these matters so sparingly in comparison with the infinite number of admirable conclusions which are demonstrated in that science. Far from pretending to teach us the constitution and motions of the heavens and the stars, with their shapes, magnitudes, and distances, the authors of the Bible intentionally forbore to speak of these things, though all were quite well known to them. [. . .]

Let us grant then that theology is conversant with the loftiest divine contemplation, and occupies the regal throne among sciences by dignity. But acquiring the highest authority in this way, if she does not descend to the lower and humbler speculations of the subordinate sciences and has no regard for them because they are not concerned with blessedness, then her professors should not arrogate to themselves the authority to decide on controversies in professions which they have neither studied nor practiced. Why, this would be as if an absolute despot, being neither a physician nor an architect but knowing himself free to command, should undertake to administer medicines and erect buildings according to his whim—at grave peril of his poor patients' lives, and the speedy collapse of his edifices.

Again, to command that the very professors of astronomy themselves see to the refutation of their own observations and proofs as mere fallacies and sophisms is to enjoin something that lies beyond any possibility of accomplishment. For this would amount to commanding that they must not see what they see and must not understand what they know, and that in searching they must find the opposite of what they actually encounter. Before this could be done they would have to be taught how to make one mental faculty command another, and the inferior powers the superior, so that the imagination and the will might be forced to believe the opposite of what the intellect understands. I am referring at all times to merely physical propositions, and not to supernatural things which are matters of faith.

I entreat those wise and prudent Fathers to consider with great care the difference that exists between doctrines subject to proof and those subject to opinion. Considering the force exerted by logical deductions, they may ascertain that it is not in the power of the professors of demonstrative sciences to change their opinions at will and apply themselves first to one side and then to the other. There is a great difference between commanding a mathematician or a philosopher and influencing a lawyer or a merchant, for demonstrated conclusions about things in nature or in the heavens cannot be changed with the same facility as opinions about what is or is not lawful in a contract, bargain, or bill of exchange. [. . .]

Now if truly demonstrated physical conclusions need not be subordinated to biblical passages, but the latter must rather be shown not to interfere with the former, then before a physical proposition is condemned it must be shown to be not rigorously demonstrated—and this is to be done not by those who hold the proposition to be true, but by those who judge it to be false. This seems very reasonable and natural, for those who believe an argument to be false may much more easily find the fallacies in it than men who consider it to be true and conclusive. Indeed, in the latter case it will happen that the more the adherents of an opinion turn over their pages, examine the arguments, repeat the observations, and compare the experiences, the more they will be confirmed in that belief. And Your Highness knows what happened to the late mathematician of the University of Pisa who undertook in his old age to look into the Copernican doctrine in the hope of shaking its foundations and refuting it, since he considered it false only because he had never studied it. As it fell out, no sooner had he understood its grounds, procedures, and demonstrations than he found himself persuaded, and from an opponent he became a very staunch defender of it. I might also name other mathematicians who, moved by my latest discoveries, have confessed it necessary to alter the previously accepted system of the world, as this is simply unable to subsist any longer.

If in order to banish the opinion in question from the world it were sufficient to stop the mouth of a single man—as perhaps those men persuade themselves who, measuring the minds of others by their own, think it impossible that this doctrine should be able to continue to find adherents—then that would be very easily done. But things stand otherwise. To carry out such a decision it would be necessary not only to prohibit the book of Copernicus and the writings of other authors who follow the same opinion, but to ban the whole science of astronomy. Furthermore, it would be necessary to forbid men to look at the heavens, in order that they might not see Mars and Venus sometimes quite near the earth and sometimes very distant, the variation being so great that Venus is forty times and Mars sixty times as large at one time as another. And it would be necessary to prevent Venus being seen round at one time and forked at another, with very thin horns; as well as many other sensory observations which can never be reconciled with the Ptolemaic system in any way, but are very strong arguments for the Copernican. And to ban Copernicus now that his doctrine is daily reinforced by many new observations and by the learned applying themselves to the reading of his book, after this opinion has been allowed and tolerated for those many years during which it was less followed and less confirmed, would seem in my judgment to be a contravention of truth, and an attempt to hide and suppress her the more as she revealed herself the more clearly and plainly. Not to abolish and censure his whole book, but only to condemn as erroneous this particular proposition, would (if I am not mistaken) be a still greater detriment to the minds of men, since it would afford them occasion to see a proposition proved that it was heresy to believe. [. . .]

Regarding the state of rest or motion of the sun and earth, experience plainly proves that in order to accommodate the common people it was necessary to assert of these things precisely what the words of the Bible convey. Even in our own age, people far less primitive continue to maintain the same opinion for reasons which will be found extremely trivial if well weighed and examined, and upon the basis of experiences that are wholly false or altogether beside the point. Nor is it worth while to try to change their opinion, they being unable to understand the arguments on the opposite side, for these depend upon observations too precise and demonstrations too subtle, grounded on abstractions which require too strong an imagination to be comprehended by them. Hence even if the stability of heaven and the motion of the earth should be more than certain in the minds of the wise, it would still be necessary to assert the contrary for the preservation of belief among the all-too-numerous vulgar. Among a thousand ordinary men who might be questioned concerning these things, probably not a single one will be found to answer anything except that it looks to him as if the sun moves and the earth stands still, and therefore he believes this to be certain. But one need not on that account take the common popular assent as an argument for the truth of what is stated; for if we should examine these very men concerning their reasons for what they believe, and on the other hand listen to the experiences and proofs which induce a few others to believe the contrary, we should find the latter to be persuaded by very sound arguments, and the former by simple appearances and vain or ridiculous impressions.

It is sufficiently obvious that to attribute motion to the sun and rest to the earth was therefore necessary lest the shallow minds of the common people should become confused, obstinate, and contumacious in yielding assent to the principal articles that are absolutely matters of faith. And if this was necessary, there is no wonder at all that it was carried out with great prudence in the holy Bible. I shall say further that not only respect for the incapacity of the vulgar, but also current opinion in those times, made the sacred authors accommodate themselves (in matters unnecessary to salvation) more to accepted usage than to the true essence of things.

4.2 Letter from Cardinal Bellarmino to Paolo Foscarini, 12 April 1615; trans. Stilllman Drake, from *Discoveries and Opinions of Galileo*, 1957, pp. 162–4. New York: Doubleday

I have gladly read the letter in Italian and the essay in Latin that Your Reverence has sent me, and I thank you for both, confessing that they are filled with ingenuity and learning. But since you ask for my opinion, I shall give it to you briefly, as you have little time for reading and I for writing.

First. I say that it appears to me that Your Reverence and Sig. Galileo did prudently to content yourselves with speaking hypothetically and not positively, as I have always believed Copernicus did. For to say that assuming the earth moves and the sun stands still saves all the appearances better than eccentrics and epicycles is to speak well. This has no danger in it, and it suffices for mathematicians. But to wish to affirm that the sun is really fixed in the centre of the heavens and merely turns upon itself without travelling from east to west, and that the earth is situated in the third sphere and revolves very swiftly around the sun, is a very dangerous thing, not only by irritating all the theologians and scholastic philosophers, but also by injuring our holy faith and making the sacred Scripture false. For your Reverence has indeed demonstrated many ways of expounding the Bible, but you have not applied them specifically, and doubtless you would have had a great deal of difficulty if you had tried to explain all the passages that you yourself had cited.

Second. I say that, as you know, the Council of Trent would prohibit expounding the Bible contrary to the common agreement of the holy Fathers. And if Your Reverence would read not only all their works but the commentaries of modern writers on Genesis, Psalms, Ecclesiastes, and Joshua, you would find that all agree in expounding literally that the sun is in the heavens and travels swiftly around the earth, while the earth is far from the heavens and remains motionless in the centre of the world. Now consider whether, in all prudence, the Church could support the giving to Scripture of a sense contrary to the holy Fathers and all the Greek and Latin expositors. Nor may it be replied that this is not a matter of faith, since if it is not so with regard to the subject matter, it is with regard to those who have spoken. Thus that man would be just as much a heretic who denied that Abraham had two sons and Jacob twelve, as one who denied the virgin birth of Christ, for both are declared by the Holy Ghost through the mouths of the prophets and apostles.

Third. I say that if there were a true demonstration that the sun was in the centre of the universe and the earth in the third sphere, and that the sun did not go around the earth but the earth went around the sun, then it would be necessary to use careful consideration in explaining the Scriptures that seemed contrary, and we should rather have to say that we do not understand them than to say that something is false which had been proven. But I do not think there is any such demonstration, since none has been shown to me. To demonstrate that the appearances are saved by assuming the sun at the centre and the earth in the heavens is not the same thing as to demonstrate that in fact the sun is in the centre and the earth in the heavens. I believe that the first demonstration may exist, but I have very grave doubts about the second; and in case of doubt one may not abandon the Holy Scriptures as expounded by the holy Fathers. I add that the words 'The sun also riseth and the sun goeth down, and hasteth to the place where he ariseth' (Ecclesiastes 1:5) were written by Solomon, who not only spoke by divine inspiration, but was a man wise above all others of all created things, which wisdom he had from God; so it is not very likely that he would affirm something that was contrary to demonstrated truth, or truth that might be demonstrated. And if you tell me that Solomon spoke according to the appearances, and that it seems to us that the sun goes round when the earth turns, as it seems to one aboard ship that the beach moves away, I shall answer thus. Anyone who departs from the beach, though to him it appears that the beach moves away, yet knows that this is an error and corrects it, seeing clearly that the ship moves and not the beach; but as to the sun and earth, no sage has needed to correct the error, since he clearly experiences that the earth stands still and that his eye is not deceived when it judges the sun to move, just as he is likewise not deceived when it judges that the moon and the stars move. And that is enough for the present.

4.3 Trans. of MS G3 in Archive of the Sacred Congregation for the Doctrine of the Faith, Ser. AD EE, fols 292r, 292v, 293r; trans P. Rosenthal, from P. Redondi, *Galileo Heretic*, 1988, pp. 333–5. London: Allen Lane

Having in past days perused Signor Galileo Galilei's book entitled *The Assayer*, I have come to consider a doctrine already taught by certain ancient philosophers and effectively rejected by Aristotle, but renewed by the same Signor Galilei. And having decided to compare it with the true and undoubted Rule of revealed doctrines, I have found that in the Light of that Lantern which by the exercise and merit of our faith shines out indeed in murky places, and which more securely and more certainly than any natural evidence illuminates us, this doctrine appears false, or even (which I do not judge) very difficult and dangerous. So that he who receives the Rule as true must not falter in speech and in the judgment of more serious matters, I have therefore thought to propose it to you, Very Reverend Father, and beg you, as I am doing, to tell me its meaning, which will serve as my warning.

Therefore, the aforesaid Author, in the book cited (on page 196, line 29), wishing to explain that proposition proffered by Aristotle in so many places—that motion is the cause of heat—and to adjust it to his intention, sets out to prove that these accidents which are commonly called colors, odors, tastes, etc., on the part of the subject, in which it is commonly believed that they are found, are nothing but pure words and are only in the sensitive body of the animal that feels them. He explains this with the example of the Tickle, or let us say Titillation, caused by touching a body in certain parts, concluding that like the tickle, as far as the action goes, once having removed the animal's sensitivity, it is no different from the touch and movement that one makes on a marble statue, for everything is our subjective experience; thus, these accidents which are apprehended by our senses and are called tastes, smells, colors, etc., are not, he says, subjects as one holds them generally to be, but only our senses, since the titillation is not in the hand or in the feather, which touches, for example, the sole of the foot, but solely in the animal's sensitive organ.

But this discourse seems to me to be at fault in taking as proved that which it must prove, i.e. that in all cases the object which we feel is in us, because the act that is involved is in us. It is the same as saying: the sight with which I see the light of the sun is in me; therefore, the light of the sun is in me. What might be the meaning of such reasoning, however, I shall not pause to examine.

The author then goes on to explain his Doctrine, and does his best to demonstrate what these accidents are in relation to the object and the end of our actions; and as one can see on page 198, line 12, he begins to explain them with the atoms of Anaxagoras or of Democritus, which he calls minims or minimal particles; and in these, he says continually, are resolved the bodies, which, however, applied to our senses penetrate our substance, and according to the diversity of the touches, and the diverse shapes of those minims, smooth or rough, hard or yielding, and according to whether they are few or many, prick us differently, and piercing with greater or lesser division, or by making it easier for us to breathe, and hence our irritation or pleasure. To the more material or corporeal sense of touch, he says, the minims of earth are most appropriate. To the taste, those of water and he calls them fluids; to the smell, those of fire and he calls them fiery particles; to the hearing, those of the air; and to the sight he then attributes the light, about which he says he has little to say. And on page 199, line 25, he concludes that in order to arouse in us tastes, smells, etc., all that is needed in bodies which commonly are tasteful, odorous, etc. are sizes, many varied shapes; and that the smells, tastes, colors, etc. are nowhere but in the eyes, tongues, noses, etc., so that once having taken away those organs, the aforesaid accidents are not distinguished from atoms except in name.

Now if one admits this philosophy of accidents as true, it seems to me, that makes greatly difficult the existence of the accidents of the bread and wine which in the Most Holy Sacrament are separated from their substance; since finding again therein the terms, and the objects of touch, sight, taste, etc., one will also have to say according to this doctrine that there are the very tiny particles with which the substance of the bread first moved our senses, which if they were substantial (as Anaxagoras said, and this author seems to allow on page 200, line 28), it follows that in the Sacrament there are substantial parts of bread or wine, which is the error condemned by the Sacred Tridentine Council, Session 13, Canon 2.

Or actually, if they were only sizes, shapes, numbers, etc., as he also seems clearly to admit, agreeing with Democritus, it follows that all these are accidental modes, or, as others say, shapes of quantity. While the Sacred Councils, and especially the Trident Council in the passage cited, determine that after the Consecration there remain in the Sacrament only the Accidents of the bread and wine, he instead says that there only remains the quantity with triangular shapes, acute or obtuse, etc., and that with these accidents alone is saved the existence of accidents or sensible species—which consequence seems to me not only in conflict with the entire communion of Theologians who teach us that in the Sacrament remain all the sensible accidents of bread, wine, color, smell, and taste, and not mere words, but also, as is known, with the good *judgment* that the quantity of the substance does not remain. Again, this is inevitably repugnant to the truth of the Sacred Councils; for, whether these minims are explained with Anaxagoras or Democritus, if they remain after the Consecration there will not be less substance of the bread in a consecrated host than in an unconsecrated host, since to be corporeal substance, in their opinion, consists, in an aggregation of atoms in this or ‖ that fashion, with this or that shape, etc. But if these particles do not remain, it follows that no accident of bread remains in the consecrated Host; since other accidents do not emerge, this Author says on page 197, line 1, that shapes, sizes, movements, etc. do so, and (these being the effects of a quantity or quantum substance) it is not possible, as all philosophers and Theologians teach, to separate them in such a way that they would exist without the substance or quantity of which they are accidents.

And this is what seems to me difficult in this Doctrine; and I propose and submit it, as regards my already expressed judgment, to what you, Most Reverend Father, will be pleased to tell and to which I make obeisance.

Chapter 5: Iberian science: Navigation, empire and counter-reformation

5.1 Garcia d'Orta, *Colloquies on the Simples and Drugs of India*; trans. C. Markham, London, 1913, pp. 368–73

RUANO

Tell me the appearance of the tree, how it grows and how all is grown on one tree, for in this Greeks, Latins, and Arabs all agree, as well as the writers who have treated of the subject recently.

ORTA

All agree, with one accord, not to tell the truth, although Dioscorides may be pardoned because he wrote with false information and at a great distance, with intervening seas not navigated as they now are. He was copied by Pliny, Galen, Isidore, Avicenna, and all the Arabs. But those who write now, such as Antonio Musa and the Friars, have the greater fault, because they merely repeat in the same way without taking the trouble to ascertain things so well known as the appearance of the tree, pepper, the fruit, how it ripens and how it is gathered.

RUANO

Are all those you have mentioned in error?

ORTA

Yes, if you call saying what is not true an error.

RUANO

This being so, tell me what you have seen or heard from persons worthy of belief, and afterwards I will come with my doubts.

ORTA

The tree of the pepper is planted at the foot of another tree, generally at the foot of a palm or cachou tree. It has a small root, and grows as its supporting tree grows, climbing round and embracing it. The leaves are not numerous, nor large, smaller than an orange leaf, green, and sharp pointed, burning a little almost like betel. It grows in bunches like grapes, and only differs in the pepper being smaller in the grains, and the bunches being smaller, and always green at the time that the pepper dries. The crop is in its perfection in the middle of January. In Malabar the plant is of two kinds, one being the black pepper and the other white; and besides these there is another in Bengal called the long pepper.

RUANO

It seems to me that you abolish all the writers, ancient and modern, by this that I have heard you say. For Dioscorides says that the tree of the pepper is low, and produces a long fruit like a sheath, which they call long pepper, and inside this sheath there are small grains like gram, and that this is the perfect pepper, for at the proper time these sheaths open and discover some close clusters and the grains which we know, and that they are gathered before they are quite ripe. He says that they are sour and these are the white pepper. They are ingredients of the medicines they make for sore eyes and against poison that has been drunk, and against the bites of venomous beasts. The long pepper is strongly biting and rather bitter, owing to having been gathered before it is ripe, and is therefore efficacious for the things I mentioned. The black pepper is more suave and sharper, and more agreeable to the taste, from having been gathered at the right time, and also more aromatic than the white kind, and so it is more profitable for tempering the food. The weakest of all is the white pepper, owing to having been gathered before it is ripe. The black pepper is heavier and better. The people of the country call it BARCAMANSI because some empty grains are found amongst it. This is what Dioscorides says on the subject, at present it being unnecessary to enter upon medicinal qualities. At the end of chapter x. he says that the root is like that of *costo*. Pliny says that the trees are like junipers, and that they grow only on Mount Caucasus according to what some say, also that the seeds are like those of the juniper, and that one seed divides or goes apart from another in a small part of the pod, like figs. The prices of them was 25 *livras* for long pepper, of black 16 to 18, white 17, a *livra* equal to 3 *cruzados*. He says that pepper in its own country is wild and not planted, and that in Italy he heard of a tree which was like a myrtle, also that there is pepper in the part of Arabia called Trogoldita, which is called in the language of that country BARCAMANSI. Everything else about its use is copied from Dioscorides, so it need not be referred to here. Avicenna has two chapters, one on FULFUL, the other on DARFULFUL, which is the long pepper, and both Avicenna and Galen do no more than copy from Dioscorides, and so with Serapiam, who only has what he found in Dioscorides and Galen. Something that Paulo Egineta wrote is not relevant. These are the remarks on the subject made by the ancients. Turning to St. Isidore, he must, as a saint, be considered a high authority. He says that when the people of the country find that the pepper is ripe for gathering, they set fire to the wood for fear of serpents and burn the serpents. The pepper turns black owing to the fire applied to the wood. But I, to tell you the real truth, look upon this as a fable; so I wrote it first and then spoke. St. Isidore cannot have said this because he believed it, but to relate what others said. So I do not care to make excuses about these things, for I do not believe them. But I must tell you that I do not know for what reason you discredit such ancient doctors, and of such high authority, whose statements are confirmed by modern writers such as Mateas Silvatico, Sepulveda, Antonio Musa, the Spanish Friar, the Italian Friar, and so many others who have written on pharmacy. On this account I require you, in the name of God, to tell me only what you have seen and heard from persons well worthy of credence, confirming what you say by reasons which you know so well how to give, and finally we will consider how it is used in medicine by the physicians of this land, then I will put any necessary questions to you, and I regret if I have spoken too freely.

ORTA

In the first place, your worship must understand that pepper does not grow either on the skirt or on the slope of Mount Caucasus, as Pliny says. For there the price of pepper is higher than in any other country. This you must know, for you know how far Mount Caucasus is from Malabar or Sumatra, places where there is the greatest quantity of pepper. Nor is it like the juniper, for it is a climbing plant, while the juniper stands by itself, nor are its leaves like those of the juniper. Their shape is as I have already described to you, and the bunches grow like those of grapes. When they are green, with the berries apart and unripe, they put them into vinegar and salt. This I know very well from the testimony of my eyes. In the same way I know that the tree of long pepper grows in a land very distant from Malabar, the nearest point being 500 leagues off, for it is in Bengal and in Java. This long pepper is worth at Cochin, where there is the greatest quantity of black pepper, 5 *cruzados* the *quintal*, and four years ago at that place, when there was a greater demand for long pepper at other places, the *quintal* was worth 15 to 20 *cruzados*. The usual price of black pepper at Cochin is $2\frac{1}{2}$ *cruzados*, but in Bengal 12 *cruzados*; while the long pepper sells in Bengal at $1\frac{1}{2}$ *cruzados*. This is enough to show that the long pepper does not come from the same tree as the ordinary kind, much less is it needful for a man who has seen a thing with his eyes to give further proof of it. The white pepper comes from a tree of its own, and, to tell you the truth, there are not many but very few in Malabar or in Malacca. They put this pepper on the tables of the lords as we put salt. It is esteemed in both parts of Malabar as good against poison and for the eyes. It would be well if all that Dioscorides said was as true as that this pepper is good against poison. You will now see that these three trees are different, namely those of long, black, and white pepper. The long pepper is called PIMPILIM in Bengal. The tree of the long is no more like that of the black pepper than a bean is like an egg. The black and white pepper trees are very like each other, and only the people of the country can tell them apart, just as we cannot tell the black from the white vines unless they are bearing grapes. If you do not want to believe me, believe in these three seeds, that one is of long, the other of black, the other of white pepper. As for pepper being called BARCAMANSI no such name has ever been heard of in any of these countries, nor anything like it.

RUANO

Truly I find myself corrected, as I do not see it as the others do, it being made so clear.

ORTA

You see here the green pepper grown in clusters on this branch of a tree, and you see there another done with vinegar and salt, which you should taste before all.

RUANO

I see it all well, and now that I am corrected I see that the new writers never investigate satisfactorily. Laguna complains of the Portuguese because they do not describe these things and only care about skinning and robbing the Indians.

5.2 Nicolás Monardes, *La Historia Medicinal de las cosas que se traen de nuestras Indias Occidentales que sirven en Medicina.* Seville, 1565–74

In the year 1492 we Spaniards with the guidance of Christopher Columbus, a native of Genoa, were led to the discovery of the West Indies, now known as the New World. Since then numerous other isles have been discovered and much of the continent, including New Spain and Peru. And these many provinces, kingdoms and cities have diverse customs and things have been found there that have never been seen in any other part of the world; and there are other things which exist here but in much greater abundance over there. This applies to gold, silver, pearls, emeralds, turquoise, and other precious stones, which now arrive from those parts in quantities far greater than what is found here; especially the gold and silver, whose value in millions is astounding, quite apart from the abundance of pearls supplied to the world. From those parts also are brought parrots, monkeys, griffins, lions, falcons, hawks, tigers, wool, cotton, cochineal, hides, sugar, copper, Brazil-wood, ebony and lapis lazuli. And such is the quantity of these things which arrive every year—almost one hundred ships laden with them—that it is an amazing and unbelievable abundance.

In addition to this wealth from our West Indies come many trees, plants, herbs, roots, juices, gums, fruits, seeds, liquors and stones which have great medicinal virtues. And in these have been discovered very great effects which are far more valuable than all of the forementioned items, because bodily health is more necessary and excellent than material possessions. . . . And, as Aristotle says, it is not surprising that different plants and fruits are produced in different lands; or that trees, plants and fruits are found in one region which do not occur in another. The dictamnus grows only in Crete; mastic only in Cyprus; cinnamon, cloves, pepper and other spices only in the Moluccas. And there are many other things in various parts of the world which have never been known until our times, which the Ancients did not have, and which time, the discoverer of all things, has revealed to us to our great benefit.

And so discoveries by the Spanish of new regions, kingdoms and provinces have led to the supply of new medicines and remedies for the treatment of numerous diseases that would otherwise have remained incurable. Although these things are known to some, they are not known to all. Therefore I set out to write about all things coming from our West Indies which serve the art of medicine to remedy the illnesses and diseases which afflict us. This will be no small benefit to our contemporaries, and also to future generations. I will make the beginning for others to add to through increasing knowledge and experience.

In this city of Seville, which is the port and terminal for all of the West Indies, we are more familiar with these things than any other part of Spain, because everything arrives here first. I have benefited from this, and in the course of practising medicine in this city for 40 years, I have used the things brought from those regions and experimented with them on numerous patients, with diligence, circumspection and very great success.

5.3 Diego de Zúñiga, *In Job commentaria*, pp. 205–7. Toledo, 1584

'The earth moves from its place and its pillars tremble'.[1] It seems that this difficult text can be clarified by the Pythagorean doctrine which asserts that the earth, by its own nature, moves and that in no other way can the very varied motions of the stars be explained. According to Plutarch this doctrine was accepted by Philolaus and Heraclides of Pontus [. . .] And in our own time Copernicus has described the course of the planets in accordance with this doctrine. There is no doubt that his theory gives a much better and truer account of the positions of the planets than Ptolemy's *Almagest* or other theories. Ptolemy in fact could not explain the precession of the equinoxes; nor could he establish a definite beginning to the year, as he himself acknowledged in the second chapter of the third part of the *Almagest* [. . .] Also we now know that the sun is over 40,000 stades closer than the Ancients thought, so that neither Ptolemy nor other astronomers knew the cause of this precession. But Copernicus gives very convincing explanations of this and other phenomena by assuming that the earth is in motion. Nor does his theory conflict at all with what Solomon says in the book of *Ecclesiastes*: 'the earth abides forever'.[2] The meaning of this is that while there is a succession on earth of epochs and generations of men, the earth remains unchanged. And indeed the text says: 'one generation passes away and another generation comes, but the earth abides forever'. The text [of *Job*] is not consistent with the immobile earth of the philosophers. Nor is it contradicted by other statements in this chapter of *Ecclesiastes* and in many others of the Holy Scriptures which refer to the movement of the sun, which Copernicus regards as the immobile centre of the universe. [. . .] There is no passage in the Holy Scriptures which speaks so clearly of an immobile earth than this one does of its mobility.

---

[1] Job 9: 6.
[2] Ecclesiastes 1: 4.

5.4 Diego de Zúñiga, *Philosophia prima pars*, pp. 229ᵛ–230ᵛ. Toledo, 1597

As for the situation of the earth, this is a matter of greater difficulty, and there is no certainty about it however much the most learned men, Aristotle, Ptolemy and many other philosophers and astronomers have tried to demonstrate that the earth's orb is situated in the centre of the universe [. . .] because the magnitude of the heavens could be so great that the appearances viewed from earth would be the same whether the earth was situated at the centre or very distant from it. And this is clear from Copernicus' great treatise. . . . It can be supposed that the extent and elevation of the universe are greater than anyone has ever thought. Now we come to the state of the earth on which there is great controversy amongst the learned; nevertheless the earth's state can be discussed with greater probability than its position. That the earth is not at rest but by its nature moves was asserted by Pythagoras and Philolaus. [. . .] In our own age the same was taught by Nicolaus Copernicus whose learned treatise based the arrangement of the universe on the multiple movement of the earth [. . .] But Aristotle, Ptolemy and other most expert philosophers and astronomers are of the opposite opinion and we follow them in this. [. . .] Some of the movements which Copernicus and others give to the earth are not problematic. But that is not the case with the alleged rotation of the entire earth in twenty-four hours, which seems to reduce the idea of the earth's motion to absurdity. Pythagoras was forced to adopt this view once he accepted that [. . .] the sun remained at rest at the centre; and since the sun does not move, the diurnal movement was attributed to the earth rotating about its centre. This was taught by Phythagoreans and Copernicus. Aristotle and Ptolemy refute this motion with persuasive arguments. The circumference of the earth is 80,181 stades. [. . .] Consequently every point on the earth's surface would traverse so much space in a day and with such a rapid motion from west to east that it would exceed the speed of clouds, birds and all other things suspended in the air, and all of these would appear to move to the west. Similarly it would be much more difficult to throw a lance or a stone to the east than towards the west [. . .] and heavy objects thrown straight up would never return to the same place, if the earth moved with such impetus; yet if this is repeated a thousand times, the objects always fall perpendicularly down; therefore the earth does not move.

5.5 Gaspar de Quiroga, *Index et Catalogus Librorum prohibitorum*. Madrid, 1583

. . . The following are all prohibited: books, treatises, documents, recipes and registers for invoking demons in any manner, whether by necromancy, hydromancy, pyromancy, aeromancy, onomancy, chiromancy and geomancy; or by writings on the magic art, witchcraft, omens, incantations, spells, circles, characters, seals, rings and figures.

Also prohibited are all books, treatises and writings which discuss or give rules, or expound the art or science of acquiring from the stars or from the lines on the hand knowledge of the future, which depends on man's freewill and chance. [. . .] It is forbidden for anyone to make predictions on such things. But this does not apply to those parts of astrology which concern general events of the world, nor those parts which teach us to know our inclinations, conditions and bodily qualities; nor to those parts of astrology which have a bearing on agriculture, navigation and medicine. . . . As for the conjurations and exorcism used against demons and storms, apart from what is authorised by Rome in prayer, only texts from ecclesiastical manuals may be used which have been inspected and approved by Ordinaries.

Chapter 6: Science from the earth in central Europe

6.1 Ulrich Rülein von Calw, 'On the Origin of Metals', from *Ein nützlich Bergbüchlein, c.*1500; trans. Herbert Clark Hoover and Lou Henry Hoover 1912, from Georg Agricola, *De Re Metallica,* 1556. New York: Dover reprint, 1950, pp. 44–6 n.

The first chapter or first part; on the common origin of ore, whether silver, gold, tin, copper, iron, or lead ore, in which they all appear together, and are called by the common name of metallic ore. It must be noticed that for the washing or smelting of metallic ore, there must be the one who works and the thing that is worked upon, or the material upon which the work is expended. The general worker (efficient force) on the ore and on all things that are born, is the heavens, its movement, its light and influences, as the philosophers say. The influence of the heavens is multiplied by the movement of the firmaments and the movements of the seven planets. Therefore, every metallic ore receives a special influence from its own particular planet, due to the properties of the planet and of the ore, also due to properties of heat, cold, dampness, and dryness. Thus gold is of the Sun or its influence, silver of the Moon, tin of Jupiter, copper of Venus, iron of Mars, lead of Saturn, and quicksilver of Mercury. Therefore, metals are often called by these names by hermits and other philosophers. Thus gold is called the Sun, in Latin *Sol,* silver is called the Moon, in Latin *Luna,* as is clearly stated in the special chapters on each metal. Thus briefly have we spoken of the 'common worker' of metal and ore. But the thing worked upon, or the common material of all metals, according to the opinion of the learned, is sulphur and quicksilver, which through the movement and influence of the heavens must have become united and hardend into one metallic body or one ore. Certain others hold that through the movement and the influence of the heavens, vapours or *braden,* called mineral exhalations, are drawn up from the depths of the earth, from sulphur and quicksilver, and the rising fumes pass into the veins and stringers and are united through the effect of the planets and made into ore. Certain others hold that metal is not formed from quicksilver, because in many places metallic ore is found and no quicksilver. But instead of quicksilver they maintain a damp and cold and slimy material is set up on all sulphur which is drawn out from the earth, like your perspiration, and from that mixed with sulphur all metals are formed. Now each of these opinions is correct according to a good understanding and right interpretation; the ore or metal is formed from the fattiness of the earth as the material of the first degree (primary element), also the vapours or *braden* on the one part and the materials on the other part, both of which are called quicksilver. Likewise in the mingling or union of the quicksilver and the sulphur in the ore, the sulphur is counted the male and the quicksilver the female, as in the bearing or conception of a child. Also the sulphur is a special worker in ore or metal.

The second chapter or part deals with the general capacity of the mountain. Although the influence of the heavens and the fitness of the material are necessary to the formation of ore or metal, yet these are not enough thereto. But there must be adaptability of the natural vessel in which the ore is formed, such are the veins. [. . .] Also there must be a suitable place in the mountain which the veins and stringers can traverse.

6.2 Georgius Agricola, 'On the Origin of Metals', from *De Ortu et Causis Subterraneorum*, 1546; trans. Herbert Clark Hoover and Lou Henry Hoover, 1912, from Georgius Agricola, *De Re Metallica*, 1556. New York: Dover reprint, 1950, p. 51 n.

Having now refuted the opinions of others, I must explain what it really is from which metals are produced. The best proof that there is water in their materials is the fact that they flow when melted, whereas they are again solidified by the cold of air or water. This, however, must be understood in the sense that there is more water in them and less 'earth'; for it is not simply water that is their substance but water mixed with 'earth.' And such a proportion of 'earth' is in the mixture as may obscure the transparency of the water, but not remove the brilliance which is frequently in unpolished things. Again, the purer the mixture, the more precious the metal which is made from it, and the greater its resistance to fire. But what proportion of 'earth' is in each liquid from which a metal is made no mortal can ever ascertain, or still less explain, but the one God has known it, Who has given certain sure and fixed laws to nature for mixing and blending things together. It is a juice (*succus*) then, from which metals are formed; and this juice is created by various operations. Of these operations the first is a flow of water which softens the 'earth' or carries the 'earth' along with it, thus there is a mixture of 'earth' and water, then the power of heat works upon the mixtures so as to produce that kind of a juice. We have spoken of the substance of metals; we must now speak of their efficient cause. [. . .]

We do not deny the statement of Albertus Magnus that the mixture of 'earth' and water is baked by subterranean heat to a certain denseness, but it is our opinion that the juice so obtained is afterward solidified by cold so as to become a metal. [. . .] We grant, indeed, that heat is the efficient cause of a good mixture of elements, and also cooks this same mixture into a juice, but until this juice is solidified by cold it is not a metal. [. . .] This view of Aristotle is the true one. For metals melt through the heat and somehow become softened; but those which have become softened through heat are again solidified by the influence of cold, and, on the contrary, those which become softened by moisture are solidified by heat.

6.3 Georgius Agricola, 'On the Knowledge of the Miner'; trans. Herbert Clark Hoover and Lou Henry Hoover, 1912, from Book I of *De Re Metallica*, 1556. New York: Dover reprint, 1950

Many persons hold the opinion that the metal industries are fortuitous and that the occupation is one of sordid toil, and altogether a kind of business requiring not so much skill as labour. But as for myself, when I reflect carefully upon its special points one by one, it appears to be far otherwise. For a miner must have the greatest skill in his work, that he may know first of all what mountain or hill, what valley or plain, can be prospected most profitably, or what he should leave alone; moreover, he must understand the veins, stringers and seams in the rocks. Then he must be thoroughly familiar with the many and varied species of earths, juices, gems, stones, marbles, rocks, metals, and compounds. He must also have a complete knowledge of the method of making all underground works. Lastly, there are the various systems of assaying substances and of preparing them for smelting; and here again there are many altogether diverse methods. [. . .]

Furthermore, there are many arts and sciences of which a miner should not be ignorant. First there is Philosophy, that he may discern the origin, cause, and nature of subterranean things; for then he will be able to dig out the veins easily and advantageously, and to obtain more abundant results from his mining. Secondly, there is Medicine, that he may be able to look after his diggers and other workmen, that they do not meet with those diseases to which they are more liable than workmen in other occupations, or if they do meet with them, that he himself may be able to heal them or may see that the doctors do so. Thirdly follows Astronomy, that he may know the divisions of the heavens and from them judge the direction of the veins. Fourthly, there is the science of Surveying that he may be able to estimate how deep a shaft should be sunk to reach the tunnel which is being driven to it, and to determine the limits and boundaries in these workings, especially in depth. Fifthly, his knowledge of Arithmetical Science should be such that he may calculate the cost to be incurred in the machinery and the working of the mine. Sixthly, his learning must comprise Architecture, that he himself may construct the various machines and timber work required underground, or that he may be able to explain the method of the construction to others. Next, he must have knowledge of Drawing, that he can draw plans of his machinery. Lastly, there is the Law, especially that dealing with metals, that he may claim his own rights, that he may undertake the duty of giving others his opinion on legal matters, that he may not take another man's property and so make trouble for himself, and that he may fulfil his obligations to others according to the law. [. . .]

But let us now approach the subject we have undertaken. Since there has always been the greatest disagreement amongst men concerning metals and mining, some praising, others utterly condemning them, therefore I have decided that before imparting my instruction, I should carefully weigh the facts with a view to discovering the truth in this matter.

6.4 Georgius Agricola, 'On Assaying'; trans. Herbert Clark Hoover and Lou Henry Hoover, 1912, from Book VII of *De Re Metallica*, 1556. New York: Dover reprint, 1950

BOOK VII.

Since the Sixth Book has described the iron tools, the vessels and the machines used in mines, this Book will describe the methods of assaying ores; because it is desirable to first test them in order that the material mined may be advantageously smelted, or that the dross may be purged away and the metal made pure. Although writers have mentioned such tests, yet none of them have set down the directions for performing them, wherefore it is no wonder that those who come later have written nothing on the subject. By tests of this kind miners can determine with certainty whether ores contain any metal in them or not; or if it has already been indicated that the ore contains one or more metals, the tests show whether it is much or little; the miners also ascertain by such tests the method by which the metal can be separated from that part of the ore devoid of it; and further, by these tests, they determine that part in which there is much metal from that part in which there is little. Unless these tests have been carefully applied before the metals are melted out, the ore cannot be smelted without great loss to the owners. [. . .] Metals, when they have been melted out, are usually assayed in order that we may ascertain what proportion of silver is in a *centumpondium* of copper or lead, or what quantity of gold is in one *libra* of silver; and, on the other hand, what proportion of copper or lead is contained in a *centumpondium* of silver, or what quantity of silver is contained in one *libra* of gold. And from this we can calculate whether it will be worth while to separate the precious metals from the base metals, or not. Further, a test of this kind shows whether coins are good or are debased; and readily detects silver, if the coiners have mixed more than is lawful with the gold; or copper, if the coiners have alloyed with the gold or silver more of it than is allowable.

The method of assaying ore used by mining people, differs from smelting only by the small amount of material used. [. . .]

Both processes, however, are carried out in the same way, for just as we assay ore in a little furnace, so do we smelt it in the large furnace. Also in both cases charcoal and not wood is burned. Moreover, in the crucible when metals are tested, be they gold, silver, copper, or lead, they are mixed in precisely the same way as they are mixed in the blast furnace when they are smelted. Further, those who assay ores with fire, either pour out the metal in a liquid state, or, when it has cooled, break the crucible and clean the metal from slag; and in the same way the smelter, as soon as the metal flows from the furnace into the forehearth, pours in cold water and takes the slag from the metal with a hooked bar. Finally, in the same way that gold and silver are separated from lead in a cupel, so also are they separated in the cupellation furnace.

It is necessary that the assayer who is testing ore or metals should be prepared and instructed in all things necessary in assaying, and that he should close the doors of the room in which the assay furnace stands, lest anyone coming at an inopportune moment might disturb his thoughts when they are intent on the work. It is also necessary for him to place his balances in a case, so that when he weighs the little buttons of metal the scales may not be agitated by a draught of air, for that is a hindrance to his work.

6.5 Paracelsus, 'Man and His Body'; trans. Norbert Guterman, from Jolande Jacobi (ed.), *Paracelsus: Selected Writings*, 1951. London: Routledge and Kegan Paul

*I/8, 158**

I am writing this to prevent you from being misled in any point; please read and reread it with diligence, not with envy, not with hatred, for you are students of medicine. Also study my books, and compare my opinions with the opinions of others; then you may be guided by your own judgment

I/10, 199

I have thus far used simple language, and I cannot boast of any rhetoric or subtleties; I speak in the language of my birth and my country, for I am from Einsiedeln, of Swiss nationality, and let no one find fault with me for my rough speech. My writings must not be judged by my language, but by my art and experience, which I offer the whole world, and which I hope will be useful to the whole world. [. . .]

Man emerged from the first matrix, the maternal womb, of the Great World. This world—formed by God's hand along with all other creatures—gave birth to man in his flesh and placed him in a transient life. For this reason man became 'earthly' and 'carnal'; he received his material body from earth and water. These two elements constitute the body in its transient, animal life, which man as a natural being received from divine creation. . . . In his earthly life man consists of the four elements. Water and earth, of which his body is formed, constitute the dwelling place and the physical envelope of life. And I am not referring here to that life of

---

*References so printed relate to the source, in the Sudhoff–Matthiessen edition, of the paragraph or paragraphs they follow; to wit, the source here is to be found in Part I, volume 8, page 158 of that edition, See p. 57 for key.

the soul, which springs from the breath of God . . . but to the transient life, of the earthly kind. For we must know that man has two kinds of life—animal life and sidereal life. . . . Hence man has also an animal body and a sidereal body; and both are one, and are not separated. The relations between the two are as follows. The animal body, the body of flesh and blood, is in itself always dead. Only through the action of the sidereal body does the motion of life come into the other body. The sidereal body is fire and air; but it is also bound to the animal life of man. Thus mortal man consists of water, earth, fire, and air.

I/14, 597–8

The mysteries of the Great and the Little World are distinguished only by the form in which they manifest themselves; for they are only *one* thing, *one* being. Heaven and earth have been created out of nothingness, but they are composed of three things—*mercurius, sulphur,* and *sal.* . . . Of these same three things the planets and all the stars consist; and not only the stars but all bodies that grow and are born from them. And just as the Great World is thus built upon the three primordial substances, so man—the Little World—was composed of the same substances. Thus man, too, is nothing but mercury, sulphur, and salt. [. . .]

I/8, 280

Consider how great and noble man was created, and what greatness must be attributed to his structure! No brain can fully encompass the structure of man's body and the extent of his virtues; he can be understood only as an image of the macrocosm, of the Great Creature. Only then does it become manifest what is in him. For what is outside is also inside; and what is not outside man is not inside.

I/8, 180

6.6 Paracelsus, 'The Physician's Remedies'; trans. Norbert Guterman, from Jolande Jacobi (ed.), *Paracelsus: Selected Writings*, 1951, pp. 158–60. London: Routledge and Kegan Paul

What sense would it make or what would it benefit a physician if he discovered the origin of the diseases but could not cure or alleviate them? And since the fit manner of preparation is not to be found in pharmaceutics, we must explore further; that is to say, we must learn from alchemy. In it we find the true cause and everything that is needed. Although alchemy has now fallen into contempt and is even considered a thing of the past, the physician should not be influenced by such judgments. For many arts, such as astronomy, philosophy, and others, are also in disrepute. I am directing you, physicians, to alchemy for the preparation of the *magnalia*, for the production of the *mysteria*, for the preparation of the *arcana*, for the separation of the pure from the impure, to the end that you may obtain a flawless, pure remedy, God-given, perfect, and of certain efficacy, achieving the highest degree of virtue and power. For it is not God's design that the remedies should exist for us ready-made, boiled, and salted, but that we should boil them ourselves, and it pleases Him that we boil them and learn in the process, that we train ourselves in this art and are not idle on earth, but labour in daily toil. For it is we who must pray for our daily bread, and if He grants it to us, it is only through our labour, our skill and preparation.

I/10, 277

The first and highest book of medicine is called *Sapientia*. Without this book no one will achieve anything fruitful. . . . For this book is God himself. In Him who has created all things lies also wisdom, and only He knows the primal cause of all things. . . . Although the remedy is given by nature . . . it must be revealed to us by the all-highest book, so that we may learn what is in it, how it is made, how it is obtained from the earth, and how and to what patients it should be administered. . . .

The second book of medicine—of this too you must take note!—is the firmament. [. . .] Just as a man reads a book on paper, so the physician is compelled to spell out the stars of the firmament in order to know his conclusions. [. . .]

I/11, 171–6

The book of medicine is nature itself. And just as you see yourself in a mirror, so you must rediscover all your sciences in nature, with exactly the same certainty and with as little illusion as when you see yourself in a mirror.

I/1, 354–5

Marvellous virtues are inherent in the remedies. One would hardly believe that nature contained such virtues. . . . For only a great artist is able to discover them, not one who is only versed in books, but only one who has acquired his ability and skill through the experience of his hands. . . . It is an important art, and therefore it cannot be clearly described, but can only be learned by experience. . . .

I/2, 430

6.7 Paracelsus, 'Alchemy, Art of Transformation'; trans. Norbert Guterman, from Jolande Jacobi (ed.), *Paracelsus: Selected Writings*, 1951. London: Routledge and Kegan Paul

Nothing has been created as *ultima materia*—in its final state. Everything is at first created in its *prima materia*, its original stuff; whereupon Vulcan comes, and by the art of alchemy develops it into its final substance. . . . For alchemy means: to carry to its end something that has not yet been completed. To obtain the lead from the ore and to transform it into what it is made for. . . . Accordingly, you should understand that alchemy is nothing but the art which makes the impure into the pure through fire. . . . It can separate the useful from the useless, and transmute it into its final substance and its ultimate essence.

I/11, 188–9

The transmutation of metals is a great mystery of nature. However laborious and difficult this task may be, whatever impediments and obstacles may lie in the way of its accomplishment, this transmutation does not go counter to nature, nor is it incompatible with the order of God, as is falsely asserted by many persons. But the base, impure five metals— that is, copper, tin, lead, iron, and quicksilver— cannot be transmuted into the nobler, pure, and perfect metals—namely, into gold and silver—without a *tinctura*, or without the philosopher's stone. [. . .]

I/11, 356–7

The great virtues that lie hidden in nature would never have been revealed if alchemy had not uncovered them and made them visible. Take a tree, for example; a man sees it in the winter, but he does not know what it is, he does not know what it conceals within itself, until summer comes and discloses the buds, the flowers, the fruit. . . . Similarly the virtues in things remain concealed to man, unless the alchemists disclose them, as the summer reveals the nature of the tree.—And if the alchemist brings to light that which lies hidden in nature, one must know that those hidden powers are different in each thing—they are different in locusts, different in leaves, different in flowers, and different in ripe and unripe fruits. For all this is so marvellous that in form and qualities the last fruit of a tree is completely unlike the first one. . . . And each thing has not only one virtue but many, just as a flower has more than one colour, and

each colour has in itself the most diverse hues; and yet they
I/8, 191–2
constitute a unity, one thing.

Alchemy is a necessary, indispensable art. . . . It is an art,
and Vulcan is its artist. He who is a Vulcan has mastered
this art; he who is not a Vulcan can make no headway in it.
But to understand this art, one must above all know that
God has created all things; and that He has created something
out of nothing. This something is a seed, in which the
purpose of its use and function is inherent from the beginning.
And since all things have been created in an unfinished state,
nothing is finished, but Vulcan must bring all things to their
completion. Things are created and given into our hands,
but not in the ultimate form that is proper to them. For
example, wood grows of itself, but does not transform itself
into boards or charcoal. Similarly, clay does not of itself
become a pot. This is true of everything that grows in
I/11, 186–7
nature.

The *quinta essentia* is that which is extracted from a
substance—from all plants and from everything which has
life—then freed of all impurities and all perishable parts,
refined into highest purity and separated from all elements. . . .
The inherency of a thing, its nature, power, virtue, and
curative efficacy, without any . . . foreign admixture . . . that
is the *quinta essentia*. It is a spirit like the life spirit, but with
this difference that the *spiritus vitae*, the life spirit, is
imperishable, while the spirit of man is perishable . . . The
quinta essentia being the life spirit of things, it can be extracted
only from the perceptible, that is to say material, parts, but
not from the imperceptible, animated parts of things. . . . It
is endowed with extraordinary powers and perfections, and
in it is found a great purity, through which it effects an
alteration or cleansing in the body, which is an incomparable
marvel. . . . Thus the *quinta essentia* can cleanse a man's
life. . . . Therefore each disease requires its own *quinta
essentia*, although some forms of the *quinta essentia* are said
I/3, 118–20
to be useful in all diseases. [. . .]

But to write more about this mystery is forbidden and
further revelation is the prerogative of the divine power.
For this art is truly a gift of God. Wherefore not everyone
can understand it. For this reason God bestows it upon
whom He pleases, and it cannot be wrested from Him by
force; for it is His will that He alone shall be honoured in it
I/14, 431
and that through it His name be praised for ever and ever.

Key to sources

The following summary of the Sudhoff–Matthiessen edition, based on the tables of contents of the volumes, provides the Paracelsian title of each source. The page number given is the initial page number for the item.

Sudhoff, Karl and Matthiessen, Wilhelm, eds. *Paracelsus. Sämtliche Werke*. Part I: Medizinische, naturwissenschaftliche und philosophische Schriften. Vols 6–9, Munich: O. W. Barth, 1922–5; vols. 1–5, 10–14, Munich, Berlin: R. Oldenbourg, 1928–33.

Volume 1. Earliest Works, *c*.1520

Von den Podagrischen Krankheiten und was ihnen anhängig, 345.

Volume 2. Works Written in Southwestern Germany, 1525–6

Das siebente Buch in der Arznei, von den Krankheiten die der Vernunft berauben, de morbis, amentium, 395.

Volume 8. Works Written in the Upper Palatinate, Regensburg, Bavaria, and Swabia, 1530

Das Buch Paragranum, letze Bearbeitung in vier Büchern, 133.

Von den Hinfallenden Siechtagen (de Caducis, Epilepsie) vier Paragraphen. Erst Ausarbeitung, 261.

Volume 10. Writings Composed in Swabia and Bavaria, 1536

Das erste Buch der Grossen Wundarznei, 7.

Das zweite Buch der Grossen Wundarznei, 215.

Volume 11. 1537–41

Sieben Defensiones. Verantwortung über etliche Verunglimpfungen seiner Missgönner, 123.

Labyrinthus medicorum errantium. Vom Irrgang der Ärtze, 161.

Die 9 Bücher de Natura rerum, an Johansen Winkelsteiner zu Freiburg in Üchtland, 307.

Volume 14. *Philosophia Magna. Spuria*

III. Coelum philosophorum sive liber vexationum (fixationum), 405.

Manuale de lapide philosophico medicinali, 421.

De Pestilitate, 597.

Chapter 7: French science in the seventeenth century

7.1 R. Descartes, *Discourse on Method*, Penguin edn., 1960, pp. 49–52

In my early youth, I had made some study of logic in philosophy, and of geometry and algebra in mathematics, and it seemed that these three arts or sciences should contribute something to my design. But, when I examined them more closely, I saw that, as for logic, its syllogisms and most of its other modes of instruction rather serve to explain to others what one knows already, or even, as in the art of Lully, to speak without judgement of what one does not know, than to acquire knowledge. And, although logic indeed contains many very true and excellent precepts, these are so confounded with so many others that are either harmful or superfluous that it is as difficult to distinguish the former as it would be to conjure up a statue of Diana or Minerva from an untouched block of marble. Then, with regard to the geometrical analysis of the ancients and the algebra of the moderns, besides the fact that both only deal with what is highly abstract and seems of no practical use, the former is so bound to the inspection of figures that it cannot exercise the understanding without greatly fatiguing the imagination, while the other is so subject to certain rules and a certain notation that it has become a confused and obscure art, which clogs the mind, rather than a science which cultivates its powers. That is why I thought I must look for some other method which would combine the advantages of these three disciplines, and yet be exempt from their defects. And, as a multiplicity of laws often provides excuses for vice, so that a State is much better governed when its few laws are very strictly observed, so, in place of the many precepts of which logic is composed, I thought I should have enough with the four following rules, provided I took a firm and constant resolution never once to fail to observe them.

The first rule was to accept as true nothing that I did not know to be evidently so: that is to say, to avoid carefully precipitancy and prejudice, and to apply my judgements to nothing but that which showed itself so clearly and distinctly to my mind that I should never have occasion to doubt it.

The second was to divide each difficulty I should examine into as many parts as possible, and as would be required the better to solve it.

The third was to conduct my thoughts in an orderly fashion, starting with what was simplest and easiest to know, and rising little by little to the knowledge of the most complex, even supposing an order where there is no natural precedence among the objects of knowledge.

The last rule was to make so complete an enumeration of the links in an argument, and to pass them all so thoroughly under review, that I could be sure I had missed nothing.

Those long chains of reasons, all quite simple and quite easy, which geometers are wont to employ in reaching their most difficult demonstrations, had given me occasion to imagine that all the possible objects of human knowledge were linked together in the same way, and that, if we accepted none as true that was not so in fact, and kept to the right order in deducing one from the other, there was nothing so remote that it could not be reached, nothing so hidden that it could not be discovered. And I was little troubled to know where to begin; for I already knew that it was by what was simplest and easiest to know; and, reflecting that among all those who have sought after truth in the sciences only the mathematicians have been able to adduce a few proofs, that is to say, certain and evident reasons, I did not doubt that I should begin with what they had investigated, although for no other benefit than to accustom my mind to nourish itself on truth. It was no part of my design, however, to attempt to learn all those particular sciences which go under the general name of mathematics. Seeing that, although they have different objects, they yet agree in all being concerned with nothing but the relations or proportions between terms, I thought it best simply to consider these proportions in general, without considering their existence except in objects which gave me knowledge of them, and without even restricting them to these objects so as to be the better able to apply them wherever they should fit. Then, as I became aware that, in order to know them, I should sometimes have to consider each one in particular, and sometimes only keep them in my memory, or take several together, I thought that, the better to consider each separately, I should represent them as straight lines, which was the simplest way I could think of and the most easily grasped by my imagination and my senses, but that, in order to retain them in my memory, or to take several together, I should explain them by certain symbols which should be as concise as possible. And in this way I thought I should be able to borrow the best there is in both geometrical analysis and algebra, and to correct the defects of the one by the other.

Indeed, I venture to say that the exact observance of the few rules I had chosen made it so easy for me to disentangle all the problems raised by these two sciences that, within the two or three months I spent in examining them, I was able, by beginning with what was simplest and most general, and by using each discovery as a means of finding fresh truths, not only to overcome much that I had judged to be extremely difficult, but it seemed to me that, even in matters of which I was ignorant, I could determine in what way, and to what extent, a solution might be found. Nor will this seem vanity on my part, if you consider that, as there is only one truth about anything, he who discovers it knows as much about the matter as can be known; thus a child who has been taught arithmetic and has done an addition according to the rules, has found out as much about the total he has been considering as the human mind can find. For, after all, the method which teaches us to follow the right order, and to enumerate exactly all the elements of a problem, covers everything but gives certainty to the rules of arithmetic.

But what pleased me most, however, about this method, was that by means of it I was sure of always using my reason, if not perfectly, at least as well as lay within my power. Besides, I felt that the practice of this method was accustoming my mind to conceiving the objects of knowledge with greater clarity and distinction, and, as it was subjected to no particular branch of learning, I promised myself that I would apply it as effectively to the difficulties of the other sciences as I had done to those of algebra. Not that I dared to undertake to investigate all these sciences from the start as they presented themselves; for that would have been contradictory to the order prescribed by my method. I had observed that the principles of these sciences must be taken from philosophy, in which, however, I found no assured principles, and I thought that my first task must be to establish such principles. But this is the most important task in the world, and the one in which haste and prejudice are most to be feared, and I felt I should not undertake it until I had reached a more mature age than the age of twenty-three, as I was at that time, and until I had spent a good deal of time in preparing myself for it, both by uprooting all the wrong notions that had hitherto inhabited my mind, and by accumulating observations to form the matter of my reasonings, and, finally, by constantly exercising myself in my prescribed method so as to strengthen myself more and more in its use.

7.2 C. Glaser, 'The purpose of early chemistry', *Traité de la Chimie*, Paris, 1663, preface; tr. anon., from *The Compleat Chymist, or a New Treatise of Chymistry*, 1677. London. Quoted in Marie Boas, *Nature and Nature's Laws*, 1970, pp. 339–42. Macmillan

The Author's Preface

Authors who have treated of chemistry have had very different discoveries and apprehensions, and thence it is that they have disagreed very much in their writings. Those who have applied themselves unto the high chemistry, and have penetrated into its greatest mysteries, have contented themselves with the knowledge thereof; and though it may seem that they wrote with an intent to be understood, yet they have penned things so obscurely, that they gave us no grounds to question whether they uttered realties, or have given us phantoms for bodies, and thorns for fruits: Others who have not soared so high, have notwithstanding had some good skill therein, and have themselves discovered some preparations, which have made them considerable to posterity; but some of these have sought their own satisfaction also, and taken pleasure to perplex men's minds, and to cast them into labyrinths, without giving them any means of retreating thence.

Others, much less capable, have yet attained some small light, but not knowing all, nor having wrought themselves what they write, and desiring for all that, to pass for sufficient artists in a profession they had learned by halves only, they made their imagination pass for certain truths, whose falsehood and imperfection the practise hath frequently discovered.

Finally, others, which deserve not the name of chemists, but rather of ignorant fireblowers, working by copies or stolen receipts, which they commonly take in some contrary sense, and having consumed their own or others' money in a ridiculous labour, have made many others accompany them in their fortunes, engaging the vulgar by promises of enriching them in certain practices, whereby they have reduced the best metal into smoke, unless perhaps they passed some part of it through their own hands, which is not the least of their operations. Hence it is that I wonder not, that many have declaimed against such authors, and against chemistry itself; not having understood truly the good things which it contains. As for myself, who profess to say nothing but what I know, and to write nothing but what I have done, I purpose only in this little treatise to publish a short and easy method for the happy attainment of all the most necessary preparations of chemistry. Those who take the pains to read and well consider it, shall observe therein nothing tedious, superfluous or defective in any point which ought to be known: and though indeed the preparations of all things cannot be found therein, yet sufficient examples thereof will be had from it. And though it was very difficult to comprise in this little tract all the discoveries which I have made in this Profession, yet I have not concealed any manual operation, and have sincerely discovered all the circumstances necessary to make a good artist, and by practice to attain the greatest knowledge thereof. I set down no preparation but what I have made and thoroughly experienced, and what any one following the rules I have prescribed, may do after me. I speak very succinctly of the theory, but I say so much therein as is necessary for directions to the preparations, and you may find in a few words the substance of many great books.

I confine myself to operations on minerals, vegetables, and animals and proceed therein orderly, and forget nothing that is necessary. I am persuaded that the experience of all that which I have advanced, will manifest my communicative freeness unto all, and that they will be well pleased with the care that I have taken therein. Unto which I have thought myself so much the more obliged by the choice which Mr. Vallot, his Majesty's chief and most worthy physician, hath made of me, to make the public chemical lectures and preparations in the Royal Garden. For this cause I have desired to manifest as well by writing as work, that I have no other design than to acknowledge the honor he hath done me, by giving satisfaction to the public, according to this inclination by all ways which are possible for me.

Of the Usefulness of Chemistry

They that have any true knowledge of this noble art, are without doubt fully persuaded of the usefulness of it; for it is the key which alone can unlock to all naturalists the door of Nature's secrets; by reducing things to their first principles;

by giving to them new forms; and by imitating Nature in all its productions and physical alterations. Without it physicians would be at a stand how to penetrate into the many fermentations, effervescences, distillations and other operations, which are performed in the body of man, and are the immediate cause of many grievous distempers, to which art the same physicians must be beholden for the remedy as well as the knowledge of the disease; for we must own that chemistry does furnish us with the more effectual medicines for the more inveterate and obstinate affections, and often supply the failings and deficiencies of those of the vulgar pharmacy. Surgeons likewise cannot be without chemistry, nor can with good success undertake the cure of all diseases pertaining to their art without chemical remedies, and knowledge of their operations: and it is impossible that apothecaries should make their compositions like true artists, if they knew not how to preserve the principal virtue of their ingredients, and separate the pure from the impure and heterogeneous in natural commixtures, as unprofitable to their intention, which is not learned without the aid of this noble and excellent art. Finally, most of the ingenuous mechanic arts are beholden to this: painters have from it their most lively and glorious colors; engravers cannot work without the assistance of these corrosive spirits prepared by chemistry; dyers cannot exalt their colors without the instructions of chemists, one might allege an infinity of other such examples, which might prove the necessity of this art; but we omit them for brevity's sake.

This art is of a very great extent, since it embraces for its subject the bodies of the three families, animal, vegetable and mineral; which by fire it reduces into different substances, which the philosophers call *first principles* and do constitute five of them, of which three are active, and two passive. The active are, the spirit which is called Mercury, the oil which is called Sulphur, and the salt, which has no other name. The passive principles are the water or phlegm, and the earth or terrestrial part. These names are bestowed upon them for the likeness they have to common Mercury, Sulphur and Salt, and the elementary water and earth: the Mercury appears to us in the resolution of bodies, in the form of a most aerial, subtle liquor; the Sulphur is apparent to our smell and taste, by which we distinguish it from the insipid and inodorous Phlegm, which sometimes ascends with it; and it appears to us in the form of a penetrating, inflammable oil; the salt remains joined to the body of the earth till it be extracted by elevation. Now while these principles remain in the body of the mixt [combination of substances], those that are active are confounded with the passive, so that their virtue is hidden, and, as it were, buried; but chemistry coming to separate them, purifies each by itself, then unites them again, to make of them bodies much purer, and more active than they were before.

7.3 B. Pascal, *Story of the Great Experiment on the Equilibrium of Fluids*, 1648; trans. I. H. B. and A. G. H. Spiers, from *The Physical Treatises of Pascal*, 1973, pp. 97–112 *passim*. New York: Octagon Books

Copy of the Account of the Experiment submitted by Monsieur Perier

The weather on Saturday last, the nineteenth of this month, was very unsettled. At about five o'clock in the morning, however, it seemed sufficiently clear; and since the summit of the Puy de Dôme was then visible, I decided to go there to make the attempt. To that end I notified several people of standing in this town of Clermont, who had asked me to let them know when I would make the ascent. Of this company some were clerics, others laymen. Among the clerics was the Very Revd. Father Bannier, one of the Minim Fathers of this city, who has on several occasions been 'Corrector' (that is, Father Superior), and the Monsieur Mosnier, Canon of the Cathedral Church of this city; among the laymen were Messieurs La Ville and Begon, councillors to the Court of Aids, and Monsieur La Porte, a doctor of medicine, practising here. All these men are very able, not only in the practice of their professions, but also in every field of intellectual interest. It was a delight to have them with me in this fine work.

On that day, therefore, at eight o'clock in the morning, we started off all together for the garden of the Minim Fathers, which is almost the lowest spot in the town, and there began the experiment in this manner.

First, I poured into a vessel six pounds of quicksilver which I had rectified during the three days preceding; and having taken glass tubes of the same size, each four feet long and hermetically sealed at one end but open at the other, I placed them in the same vessel and carried out with each of them the usual vacuum experiment. Then, having set them up side by side without lifting them out of the vessel, I found that the quicksilver left in each of them stood at the same level, which was twenty-six inches and three and a half lines above the surface of the quicksilver in the vessel. I repeated this experiment twice at this same spot, in the same tubes, with the same quicksilver, and in the same vessel; and found in each case that the quicksilver in the two tubes stood at the same horizontal level, and at the same height as in the first trial.

That done, I fixed one of the tubes permanently in its vessel for continuous experiment. I marked on the glass the height of the quicksilver, and leaving that tube where it stood, I requested Revd. Father Chastin, one of the brothers of the house, a man as pious as he is capable, and one who reasons very well upon these matters, to be so good as to observe from time to time all day any changes that might occur. With the other tube and a portion of the same quicksilver, I then proceeded with all these gentlemen to the top of the Puy de Dôme, some 500 fathoms above the Convent. There, after I had made the same experiments in the same way that I had made them at the Minims, we found that there remained in the tube, a height of only twenty-three inches and two lines of quicksilver; whereas in the same tube, at the Minims we had found a height of twenty-six inches and three and a half lines. Thus between the heights of the quicksilver in the two experiments there proved to be a difference of three inches one line and a half. We were so carried away with wonder and delight, and our surprise was so great that we wished, for our own satisfaction, to repeat the experiment. So I carried it out with the greatest care five times more at different points on the summit of the mountain, once in the shelter of the little chapel that stands there, once in the open, once shielded from the wind, once in the wind, once in fine weather, once in the rain and fog which visited us occasionally. Each time I most carefully rid the tube of air; and in all these experiments we invariably found the same height of quicksilver. This was twenty-three inches and two lines, which yields the same discrepancy of three inches, one line and a half in comparison with the twenty-six inches, three lines and a half which had been found at the Minims. This satisfied us fully.

Later, on the way down at a spot called Lafon de l'Arbre, far above the Minims but much farther below the top of the mountain, I repeated the same experiment, still with the same tube, the same quicksilver, and the same vessel, and there found that the height of the quicksilver left in the tube was twenty-five inches. I repeated it a second time at the same spot; and Monsieur Mosnier, one of those previously mentioned, having the curiosity to perform it himself, then did so again, at the same spot. All these experiments yielded the same height of twenty-five inches, which is one inch, three lines and a half less than that which we had found at the Minims, and one inch and ten lines more than we had just found at the top of the Puy de Dôme. It increased our satisfaction not a little to observe in this way that the height of the quicksilver diminished with the altitude of the site.

On my return to the Minims I found that the [quicksilver in the] vessel I had left there in continuous operation was at the same height at which I had left it, that is, at twenty-six inches, three lines and a half; and the Revd. Father Chastin, who had remained there as observer, reported to us that no change had occurred during the whole day, although the weather had been very unsettled, now clear and still, now rainy, now very foggy, and now windy.

Here I repeated the experiment with the tube I had carried to the Puy de Dôme, but in the vessel in which the tube used for the continuous experiment was standing. I found that the quicksilver was at the same level in both tubes and exactly at the height of twenty-six inches, three lines and a half, at which it had stood that morning in this same tube, and as it had stood all day in the tube used for the continuous experiment.

I repeated it again a last time, not only in the same tube I had used on the Puy de Dôme, but also with the same quicksilver and in the same vessel that I had carried up the mountain; and again I found the quicksilver at the same height of twenty-six inches, three lines and a half which I had observed in the morning, and thus finally verified the certainty of our results.

Chapter 8: Science in seventeenth-century England

8.1 W. Gilbert, *De Magnete*, 1600; trans. P. Fleury Mottelay. New York: Dover edn., 1958, pp. 23–5, 327, 333–5 *passim*

The magnetic poles may be found in every loadstone, whether strong and powerful (male, as the term was in antiquity) or faint, weak, and female; whether its shape is due to design or to chance, and whether it be long, or flat, or four-square, or three-cornered, or polished; whether it be rough, broken-off, or unpolished: the loadstone ever has and ever shows its poles. But inasmuch as the spherical form, which, too, is the most perfect, agrees best with the earth, which is a globe, and also is the form best suited for experimental uses, therefore we purpose to give our principal demonstrations with the aid of a globe-shaped loadstone, as being the best and the most fitting. Take then a strong loadstone, solid, of convenient size, uniform, hard, without flaw; on a lathe, such as is used in turning crystals and some precious stones, or on any like instrument (as the nature and toughness of the stone may require, for often it is worked only with difficulty), give the loadstone the form of a ball. The stone thus prepared is a true homogeneous offspring of the earth and is of the same shape, having got from art the orbicular form that nature in the beginning gave to the earth, the common mother; and it is a natural little body endowed with a multitude of properties whereby many abstruse and unheeded truths of philosophy, hid in deplorable darkness, may be more readily brought to the knowledge of mankind. To this round stone we give the name Μικρόγη (microge) or Terrella (earthkin, little earth).[1]

To find, then, poles answering to the earth's poles, take in your hand the round stone, and lay on it a needle or a piece of iron wire. the ends of the wire move round their middle point, and suddenly come to a standstill. Now, with ochre or with chalk, mark where the wire lies still and sticks. Then move the middle or centre of the wire to another spot, and so to a third and a fourth, always marking the stone along the length of the wire where it stands still: the lines so marked will exhibit meridian circles, or circles like meridians on the stone or terrella; and manifestly they will all come together at the poles of the stone. The circles being continued in this way, the poles appear, both the north and the south, and betwixt these, midway, we may draw a large circle for an equator, as is done by the astronomer in the heavens and on his spheres and by the geographer on the terrestrial globe; for the line so drawn on this our terrella is also of much utility in our demonstrations and our magnetic experiments. Poles

---

[1] Sir Kenelm Digby, 'A Treatise of Bodies', London, 1645, Chap. XX, p. 225.

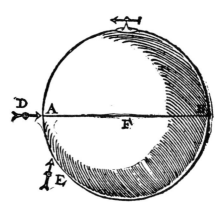

are also found in the round stone, in a versorium, in a piece of iron touched with a loadstone and resting on a needle or point (attached at its base to the terrella), so that it can freely revolve, as in the figure. [. . .]

On top of the stone *AB* is set the versorium in such a way that its pointer may remain in equilibrium: mark with chalk the direction of the pointer when at rest. Then move the instrument to another spot and again mark the direction in which the pointer looks; repeat this many times at many different points and you will, from the convergence of the lines of direction, find one pole at the point *A*, the other at *B*. A pointer also indicates the true pole if brought near to the stone, for it eagerly faces the stone at right angles, and seeks the pole itself direct and turns on its axis in a right line toward the centre of the stone. Thus the pointer *D* regards *A* and *F*, the pole and the centre, but the pointer *E* looks not straight either toward the pole *A* or the centre *F*. A bit of fine iron wire as long as a barley-corn is laid on the stone and is moved over the zones and the surface of the stone till it stands perpendicularly erect; for at the poles, whether N. or S., it stands erect; but the farther it is from the poles (towards the equator) the more it inclines. The poles thus found, you are to mark with a sharp file or a gimlet. [. . .]

[. . .] We infer, not with mere probability, but with certainty, the diurnal rotations of the earth; for nature ever acts with fewer rather than with many means; and because it is more accordant to reason that the one small body, the earth, should make a daily revolution than that the whole universe should be whirled around it. I pass by the earth's other movements, for here we treat only of the diurnal rotation, whereby it turns to the sun and produces the natural day (of twenty-four hours) which we call *nycthemeron*. And, indeed, nature would seem to have given a motion quite in harmony with the shape of the earth, for the earth being a globe, it is far easier and far more fitting that it should revolve on its natural poles, than that the whole universe, whose bounds we know not nor can know, should be whirled round; easier and more fitting than that there should be fashioned a sphere of the *primum mobile*—a thing not received by the ancients, and which even Aristotle never thought of or admitted as existing beyond the sphere of the fixed stars; finally, which the holy Scriptures do not recognize, as neither do they recognize a revolution of the whole firmament. [. . .]

The earth therefore rotates, and by a certain law of necessity, and by an energy that is innate, manifest, conspicuous, revolves in a circle toward the sun; through this motion it shares in the solar energies and influences; and its verticity holds it in this motion lest it stray into every region of the sky. The sun (chief inciter of action in nature), as he causes the planets to advance in their courses, so, too, doth bring about this revolution of the globe by sending forth the energies of his spheres—his light being effused.

And were not the earth to revolve with diurnal rotation, the sun would ever hang with its constant light over a given part, and, by long tarrying there, would scorch the earth, reduce it to powder, and dissipate its substance, and the uppermost surface of earth would receive grievous hurt: nothing of good would spring from earth, there would be no vegetation; it could not give life to the animate creation, and man would perish. In other parts all would be horror, and all things frozen stiff with intense cold: hence all its eminences would be hard, barren, inaccessible, sunk in everlasting shadow and unending night. And as the earth herself cannot endure so pitiable and so horrid a state of things on either side, with her astral magnetic mind she moves in a circle, to the end there may be, by unceasing change of light, a perpetual vicissitude, heat and cold, rise and decline, day and night, morn and even, noonday and deep night. So the earth seeks and seeks the sun again, turns from him, follows him, by her wondrous magnetical energy.

And not only from the sun would ill impend, were the earth to stand still and be deprived of the benefit of his rays; from the moon also great dangers would threaten. For we see how the ocean swells and comes to flood under certain positions of the moon. But if by the daily rotation of the earth the moon did not quickly pass, the sea would rise unduly at some parts and many coasts would be overwhelmed by mighty tides. Lest the earth, then, should in divers ways perish and be destroyed, she rotates in virtue of her magnetic and primary energy. And such are the movements in the rest of the planets, the motion and light of other bodies especially urging. For the moon also turns round during its menstrual circuit that it may on all its parts successively receive the sun's light, which it enjoys, with which it is refreshed like the earth itself; nor could the moon without grave ill and sure destruction stand the unceasing incidence of the light on one of its sides only.

Thus each of the moving globes has circular motion, either in a great circular orbit or on its own axis or in both ways. But that all the fixed stars, and the planets, and all the higher heavens, still revolve simply for the earth's sake is for the mind of a philosopher a ridiculous supposition. The earth then revolves, and not the whole heavens; and this movement brings growth and decay, gives occasion for the generation of animated things, and arouses the internal heat to productiveness. Hence does matter vegetate to receive forms, and from this primary revolution of the earth natural bodies have prime incitation and original act. The motion of the whole earth, therefore, is primary, astral, circular about its poles, whose verticity rises on both sides from the plane of the equator, and the energy is infused into the opposite ends, so that the globe by a definite rotation might move to the good, sun and stars inciting. But the simple right-downward motion assumed by the Peripatetics is the movement of weight, of coacervation, of separated parts, in the ratio of their matter, by right lines toward the earth's centre, these tending to the centre by the shortest route. The motions of separate magnetical parts of the earth are, besides that of coacervation, those of coition, revolution, and direction of the parts to the whole, into harmony and agreement of the form.

8.2 W. Harvey, *De motu cordis*, 1626. Dent, Everyman edn., 1952, ch. VIII, pp. 55–7; ch. IX, pp. 58–9

OF THE QUANTITY OF BLOOD PASSING THROUGH THE HEART FROM THE VEINS TO THE ARTERIES; AND OF THE CIRCULAR MOTION OF THE BLOOD

Thus far I have spoken of the passage of the blood from the veins into the arteries, and of the manner in which it is transmitted and distributed by the action of the heart; points to which some, moved either by the authority of Galen or Columbus, or the reasonings of others, will give in their adhesion. But what remains to be said upon the quantity and source of the blood which thus passes, is of so novel and unheard-of character, that I not only fear injury to myself from the envy of a few, but I tremble lest I have mankind at large for my enemies, so much doth wont and custom, that become as another nature, and doctrine once sown and that hath struck deep root, and respect for antiquity influence all men: Still the die is cast, and my trust is in my love of truth, and the candour that inheres in cultivated minds. And sooth to say, when I surveyed my mass of evidence, whether derived from vivisections, and my various reflections on them, or from the ventricles of the heart and the vessels that enter into and issue from them, the symmetry and size of these conduits,—for nature doing nothing in vain, would never have given them so large a relative size without a purpose,—or from the arrangement and intimate structure of the valves in particular, and of the other parts of the heart in general, with many things besides, I frequently and seriously bethought me, and long revolved in my mind, what might be the quantity of blood which was transmitted, in how short a time its passage might be effected, and the like; and not finding it possible that this could be supplied by the juices of the ingested aliment without the veins on the one hand becoming drained, and the arteries on the other getting ruptured through the excessive charge of blood, unless the blood should somehow find its way from the arteries into the veins, and so return to the right side of the heart; I began to think whether there might not be a A MOTION, AS IT WERE, IN A CIRCLE. Now this I afterwards found to be true; and I finally saw that the blood, forced by the action of the left ventricle into the arteries, was distributed to the body at large, and its several parts, in the same manner as it is sent through the lungs, impelled by the right ventricle into the pulmonary artery, and that it then passed through the veins and along the vena cava, and so round to the left ventricle in the manner already indicated. Which motion we may be allowed to call circular, in the same way as Aristotle says that the air and the rain emulate the circular motion of the superior bodies; for the moist earth, warmed by the sun, evaporates; the vapours drawn upwards are condensed, and descending in the form of rain, moisten the earth again; and by this arrangement are generations of living things produced; and in like manner too are tempests and meteors engendered by the circular motion, and by the approach and recession of the sun.

And so, in all likelihood, does it come to pass in the body, through the motion of the blood; the various parts are nourished, cherished, quickened by the warmer, more perfect, vaporous, spirituous, and, as I may say, alimentive blood; which, on the contrary, in contact with these parts becomes cooled, coagulated, and, so to speak, effete; whence it returns to its sovereign the heart, as if to its source, or to the inmost home of the body, there to recover its state of excellence or perfection. Here it resumes its due fluidity and receives an infusion of natural heat—powerful, fervid, a kind of treasury of life, and is impregnated with spirits, and it might be said with balsam; and thence it is again dispersed; and all this depends on the motion and action of the heart.

The heart, consequently, is the beginning of life; the sun of the microcosm, even as the sun in his turn might well be designated the heart of the world; for it is the heart by whose virtue and pulse the blood is moved, perfected, made apt to nourish, and is preserved from corruption and coagulation; it is the household divinity which, discharging its function, nourishes, cherishes, quickens the whole body, and is indeed the foundation of life, the source of all action. [. . .]

THAT THERE IS A CIRCULATION OF THE BLOOD IS CONFIRMED FROM THE FIRST PROPOSITION

But lest any one should say that we give them words only, and make mere specious assertions without any foundation, and desire to innovate without sufficient cause, three points present themselves for confirmation, which being stated, I conceive that the truth I contend for will follow necessarily, and appear as a thing obvious to all. First,—the blood is incessantly transmitted by the action of the heart from the vena cava to the arteries in such quantity, that it cannot be supplied from the ingesta, and in such wise that the whole mass must very quickly pass through the organ; Second,—the blood under the influence of the arterial pulse enters and is impelled in a continuous, equable, and incessant stream through every part and member of the body, in much larger quantity than were sufficient for nutrition, or than the whole mass of fluids could supply; Third,—the veins in like manner return this blood incessantly to the heart from all parts and members of the body. These points proved, I conceive it will be manifest that the blood circulates, revolves, propelled and then returning, from the heart to the extremities, from the extremities to the heart, and thus that it performs a kind of circular motion.

Let us assume either arbitrarily or from experiment, the quantity of blood which the left ventricle of the heart will contain when distended to be, say two ounces, three ounces, one ounce and a half—in the dead body I have found it to hold upwards of two ounces. Let us assume further, how much less the heart will hold in the contracted than in the dilated state; and how much blood it will project into the aorta upon each contraction;—and all the world allows that with the systole something is always projected, a necessary consequence demonstrated in the third chapter, and obvious from the structure of the valves; and let us suppose as approaching the truth that the fourth, or fifth, or sixth, or even but the eighth part of its charge is thrown into the artery at each contraction; this would give either half an ounce, or three drachms, or one drachm of blood as propelled by the heart at each pulse into the aorta; which quantity, by reason of the valves at the root of the vessel, can by no means return into the ventricle. Now, in the course of half an hour, the heart will have made more than one thousand beats, in some as many as two, three, or even four thousand. Multiplying the number of drachms propelled by the number of pulses, we shall have either one thousand half-ounces, or one thousand times three drachms, or a like proportional quantity of blood, according to the amount which we assume as propelled with each stroke of the heart, sent from this organ into the artery; a larger quantity in every case than is contained in the whole body! In the same way, in the sheep or dog, say that but a single scruple of blood passes with each stroke of the heart, in one half-hour we should have one thousand scruples, or about three pounds and a half of blood injected into the aorta; but the body of neither animal contains above four pounds of blood, a fact which I have myself ascertained in the case of the sheep.

Upon this supposition, therefore, assumed merely as a ground for reasoning, we see the whole mass of blood passing through the heart, from the veins to the arteries, and in like manner through the lungs.

8.3 R. Boyle, *Of the Excellency and Grounds of the Corpuscular Philosophy*, London, 1674; abridged by Peter Shaw, 1725, Vol. II, pp. 187–96; quoted by Marie Boas, *Nature and Nature's Laws*, 1970, pp. 311–17 *passim*. Macmillan

Of the Excellency and Grounds of the Corpuscular or Mechanical Philosophy

By embracing the corpuscular or mechanical philosophy, I am far from supposing with the Epicureans that atoms accidentally meeting in an infinite vacuum were able, of themselves, to produce a world and all its phenomena: nor do I suppose, when God had put into the whole mass of matter an invariable quantity of motion, he needed do no more to make the universe; the material parts being able, by their own unguided motions, to throw themselves into a regular system.

The philosophy I plead for reaches but to things purely corporeal; and distinguishing between the first origin of things and the subsequent course of nature, teaches that God indeed gave motion to matter; but that, in the beginning, he so guided the various motion of the parts of it as to contrive them into the world he designed they should compose; and established those rules of motion, and that order amongst things corporeal, which we call the laws of nature. Thus the universe being once framed by God and the laws of motion settled and all upheld by his perpetual concourse and general providence; the same philosophy teaches, that the phenomena of the world are physically produced by the mechancial properties of the parts of matter, and, that they operate upon one another according to mechanical laws. 'Tis of this kind of corpuscular philosophy, that I speak.

And the first thing that recommends it is the intelligibleness or clearness of its principles and explanations. [. . .]

I next observe that there cannot be fewer principles than the two grand ones of our philosophy, matter and motion; for matter alone, unless it be moved, is wholly unactive; and, whilst all the parts of a body continue in one state, without motion, that body will not exercise any action, or suffer any alteration; though it may, perhaps, modify the action of other bodies that move against it.

Nor can we conceive any principles more primary than matter and motion: for either both of them were immediately created by God; or, if matter be eternal, motion must either be produced by some immaterial supernatural agent; or it must immediately flow, by way of emanation, from the nature of the matter it appertains to.

There cannot be any physical principles more simple than matter and motion; neither of them being resoluble into any other thing.

The next thing which recommends the corpuscular principles is their extensiveness. The genuine and necessary effect of the strong motion of one part of matter against another is either to drive it on, in its entire bulk, or to break and divide it into particles of a determinate motion, figure, size, posture, rest, order or texture. The two first of these, for instance, are each of them capable of numerous varieties: for the figure of a portion of matter may either be one of the five regular geometrical figures, some determinate species of solid figures, or irregular, as the grains of sand, feathers, branches, files etc. And, as the figure, so the motion of one of these particles may be exceedingly diversified, not only by the determination to a particular part of the world but by several other things: as by the almost infinitely different degrees of celerity; by the manner of its progression, with or without rotation, etc. and more yet by the line wherein it moves; as circular, elliptical, parabolical, hyperbolical, spiral, etc. For, as later geometricians have shown that these curves may be compounded of several motions, that is, described by a body whose motion is mixed, and results from two or more simple motions; so, how many more curves may be made by new compositions, and re-compositions of motion, is not easy to determine.

Now, since a single particle of matter, by virtue of only two mechanical properties that belong to it, may be diversified so many ways; what a vast number of variations may we suppose capable of being produced by the compositions, and recompositions of myriads of single invisible corpuscles, that may be contained and concreted in one small body; and each of them be endued with more than two or three of the fertile, universal principles above-mentioned? And the aggregate of those corpuscles may be further diversified by the texture resulting from their convention into a body; which, as so made up, has its own magnitude, shape, pores, and many capacities of acting and suffering, upon account of the place it holds among other bodies, in a world constituted like ours: so that, considering the numerous diversifications that compositions and re-compositions may make of a small number, those who think the mechanical principles may serve, indeed, to account for the phenomena of some particular part of natural philosophy, as statics, the theory of planetary motions etc. but prove unapplicable to all the phenomena of things corporeal seem to imagine, that by putting together the letters of the alphabet one may, indeed, make up all the words to be found in Euclid or Virgil, or in the Latin or English language, but that they can by no means supply words to all the books of a great library; much less, to all the languages in the world. [. . .]

I come now to consider that which I observe most alienates other sects from the mechanical philosophy; viz. a supposition, that it pretends to have principles so universal and mathematical that no other physical hypothesis can be tolerated by it.

This I look upon as an easy, indeed but an important mistake: for the mechanical principles are so universal, and appliable to so many purposes, that they are rather fitted to take in, than to exclude, any other hypothesis founded on nature. And such hypotheses, if prudently considered, will be found, as far as they have truth on their side, to be either legitimately deducible from the mechanical principles or fairly reconcileable to them. For such hypotheses will, probably, attempt to account for the phenomena of nature, either by the help of a determinate number of material ingredients, such as the *tria prima* of the chymists, or else by introducing some general agents, as the Platonic soul of the world, and the universal spirit, asserted by some chymists; or, by both these ways together.

Now, the chief thing that a philosopher should look after, in explaining difficult phenomena, is not so much what the agent is or does as, what changes are made in the patient, to bring it to exhibit the phenomena proposed; and by what means, and after what manner, those changes are effected. So that the mechanical philosopher being satisfied, one part of matter can act upon another, only by virtue of local motion, or the effects and consequences thereof; he considers, if the proposed agent be not intelligible and physical, it can never physically explain the phenomena; and if it be intelligible and physical, it will be reducible to matter and some or other of its universal properties. And the indefinite divisibility of matter, the wonderful efficacy of motion, and the almost infinite variety of coalitions, and structures that may be made of minute and insensible corpuscles being duly weighed; why may not a philosopher think it possible to make out, by their help, the mechanical possibility of any corporeal agent, how subtle, diffused, or active soever, that can be solidly proved to have a real existence in nature?

8.4 I. Newton, *Opticks*, 1730 edn. New York: Dover edn., 1952, pp. 26–33, 45; figs 13 (p. 27), 18 (p. 47). Newton's optical experiments

PROP. II. Theor. II.

The Light of the Sun consists of Rays differently Refrangible.

The Proof by Experiments.

Exper. 3

In a very dark Chamber, at a round Hole, about one third Part of an Inch broad, made in the Shut of a Window, I placed a Glass Prism, whereby the Beam of the Sun's Light, which came in at that Hole, might be refracted upwards toward the opposite Wall of the Chamber, and there form a colour'd Image of the Sun. The Axis of the Prism (that is, the Line passing through the middle of the Prism from one end of it to the other end parallel to the edge of the Refracting Angle) was in this and the following Experiments perpendicular to the incident Rays. About this Axis I turned the Prism slowly, and saw the refracted Light on the Wall, or coloured Image of the Sun, first to descend, and then to ascend. Between the Descent and Ascent, when the Image seemed Stationary, I stopp'd the Prism, and fix'd it in that Posture, that it should be moved no more. For in that Posture the Refractions of the Light at the two Sides of the refracting Angle, that is, at the Entrance of the Rays into the Prism, and at their going out of it, were equal to one another.

So also in other Experiments, as often as I would have the Refractions on both sides the Prism to be equal to one another, I noted the Place where the Image of the Sun formed by the refracted Light stood still between its two contrary Motions, in the common Period of its Progress and Regress; and when the Image fell upon that Place, I made fast the Prism. And in this Posture, as the most convenient, it is to be understood that all the Prisms are placed in the following Experiments, unless where some other Posture is described. The Prism therefore being placed in this Posture, I let the refracted Light fall perpendicularly upon a Sheet of white Paper at the opposite Wall of the Chamber, and observed the Figure and Dimensions of the Solar Image formed on the Paper by that Light. This Image was Oblong and not Oval, but terminated with two Rectilinear and Parallel Sides, and two Semicircular Ends. On its Sides it was bounded pretty distinctly, but on its Ends very confusedly and indistinctly the Light there decaying and vanishing by degrees. The Breadth of this Image answered to the

OPTICKS:

OR, A

TREATISE

OF THE

Reflections, Refractions, Inflections and *Colours*

OF

LIGHT.

The FOURTH EDITION, *corrected.*

By Sir *ISAAC NEWTON*, Knt.

LONDON:

Printed for WILLIAM INNYS at the West-
End of St. *Paul*'s. MDCCXXX.

TITLE PAGE OF THE 1730 EDITION

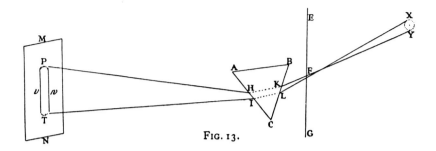

Fig. 13.

Sun's Diameter, and was about two Inches and the eighth Part of an Inch, including the Penumbra. For the Image was eighteen Feet and an half distant from the Prism, and at this distance that Breadth, if diminished by the Diameter of the Hole in the Window-shut, that is by a quarter of an Inch, subtended an Angle at the Prism of about half a Degree, which is the Sun's apparent Diameter. But the Length of the Image was about ten Inches and a quarter, and the Length of the Rectilinear Sides about eight Inches; and the refracting Angle of the Prism, whereby so great a Length was made, was 64 degrees. With a less Angle the Length of the Image was less, the Breadth remaining the same. If the Prism was turned about its Axis that way which made the Rays emerge more obliquely out of the second refracting Surface of the Prism, the Image soon became an Inch or two longer, or more; and if the Prism was turned about the contrary way, so as to make the Rays fall more obliquely on the first refracting Surface, the Image soon became an Inch or two shorter. And therefore in trying this Experiment, I was as curious as I could be in placing the Prism by the above-mention'd Rule exactly in such a Posture, that the Refractions of the Rays at their Emergence out of the Prism might be equal to that at their Incidence on it. This Prism had some Veins running along within the Glass from one end to the other, which scattered some of the Sun's Light irregularly, but had no sensible Effect in increasing the Length of the coloured Spectrum. For I tried the same Experiment with other Prisms with the same Success. And particularly with a Prism which seemed free from such Veins, and whose refracting Angle was $62\frac{1}{2}$ Degrees, I found the Length of the Image $9\frac{3}{4}$ or 10 Inches at the distance of $18\frac{1}{2}$ Feet from the Prism, the Breadth of the Hole in the Window-shut being $\frac{1}{4}$ of an Inch, as before. And because it is easy to commit a Mistake in placing the Prism in its due Posture, I repeated the Experiment four or five Times, and always found the Length of the Image that which is set down above. With another Prism of clearer Glass and better Polish, which seemed free from Veins, and whose refracting Angle was $63\frac{1}{2}$ Degrees, the Length of this Image at the same distance of $18\frac{1}{2}$ Feet was also about 10 Inches, or $10\frac{1}{8}$. Beyond these Measures for about a $\frac{1}{4}$ or $\frac{1}{3}$ of an Inch at either end of the Spectrum the Light of the Clouds seemed to be a little tinged with red and violet, but so very faintly, that I suspected that Tincture might either wholly, or in great Measure arise from some Rays of the Spectrum scattered irregularly by some Inequalities in the Substance and Polish of the Glass, and therefore I did not include it in these Measures. Now the different Magnitude of the hole in the Window-shut, and different thickness of the Prism where the Rays passed through it, and different inclinations of the Prism to the Horizon, made no sensible changes in the length of the Image. Neither did the different matter of the Prisms make any: for in a Vessel made of polished Plates of Glass cemented together in the shape of a Prism and filled with Water, there is the like Success of the Experiment according to the quantity of the Refraction. It is farther to be observed, that the Rays went on in right Lines from the Prism to the Image, and therefore at their very going out of the Prism had all that Inclination to one another from which the length of the Image proceeded, that is, the Inclination of more than two degrees and an half. And yet according to the Laws of Opticks vulgarly received, they could not possibly be so much inclined to one another.* For let EG [*Fig.* 13] represent the Window-shut, F the hole made therein through which a beam of the Sun's Light was transmitted into the darkened Chamber, and ABC a Triangular Imaginary Plane whereby the Prism is feigned to be cut transversely through the middle of the Light. Or if you please, let ABC represent the Prism it self, looking directly towards the Spectator's Eye with its nearer end: And let XY be the Sun, MN the Paper upon which the Solar Image or Spectrum is cast, and PT the Image it self whose sides towards v and w are Rectilinear and Parallel, and ends towards P and T Semicircular. YKHP and XLIT are two Rays, the first of which comes from the lower part of the Sun to the higher part of the Image, and is refracted in the Prism at K and H, and the latter comes from the higher part of the Sun to the lower part of the Image, and is refracted at L and J. Since the Refractions on both sides the Prism are equal to one another, that is, the Refraction at K equal to the Refraction at J, and the Refraction at L equal to the Refraction at H, so that the Refractions of the incident Rays at K and L taken together, are equal to the Refractions of the emergent Rays at H and J taken together: it follows by adding equal things to equal things, that the Refractions at K and H taken together, are equal to the Refractions at J and L taken together, and therefore the two Rays being equally refracted, have the same Inclination to one another after Refraction which they had before; that is, the Inclination of half a Degree answering to the Sun's Diameter. For so great was the inclination of the Rays to one another before Refraction. So then, the length of the Image PT would by the Rules of Vulgar Opticks subtend an Angle of half a Degree at the Prism, and by Consequence be equal to the breadth vw; and therefore the Image would be round. Thus it would be were the two Rays XLJT and YKHP, and all the rest which form the Image $PwTv$, alike refrangible. And therefore seeing by Experience it is found that the Image is not round, but about five times longer than broad, the Rays which going to the upper end P of the Image suffer the greatest Refraction, must be more refrangible than those which go to the lower end T, unless the Inequality of Refraction be casual.

This Image or Spectrum PT was coloured, being red at its least refracted end T, and violet at its most refracted end P, and yellow green and blue in the

---

* See our Author's *Lectiones Opticæ*, Part. I. Sect. 1. § 5.

intermediate Spaces. Which agrees with the first Proposition, that Lights which differ in Colour, do also differ in Refrangibility. The length of the Image in the foregoing Experiments, I measured from the faintest and outmost red at one end, to the faintest and outmost blue at the other end, excepting only a little Penumbra, whose breadth scarce exceeded a quarter of an Inch, as was said above. [. . .]

Exper. 6

In the middle of two thin Boards I made round holes a third part of an Inch in diameter, and in the Window-shut a much broader hole being made to let into my darkned Chamber a large Beam of the Sun's Light; I placed a Prism behind the Shut in that beam to refract it towards the opposite Wall, and close behind the Prism I fixed one of the Boards, in such manner that the middle of the refracted Light might pass through the hole made in it, and the rest be intercepted by the Board. Then at the distance of about twelve Feet from the first Board I fixed the other Board in such manner that the middle of the refracted Light which came through the hole in the first Board, and fell upon the opposite Wall, might pass through the hole in this other Board, and the rest being intercepted by the Board might paint upon it the coloured Spectrum of the Sun. And close behind this Board I fixed another Prism to refract the Light which came through the hole.

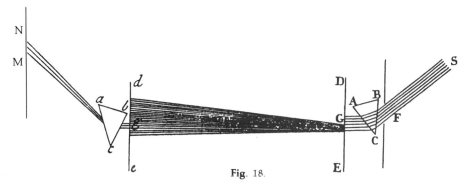

Fig. 18.

Illustration.

Let F [in *Fig.* 18] be the wide hole in the Window-shut, through which the Sun shines upon the first Prism ABC, and let the refracted Light fall upon the middle of the Board DE, and the middle part of that Light upon the hole G made in the middle part of that Board. Let this trajected part of that Light fall again upon the middle of the second Board *de*, and there paint such an oblong coloured Image of the Sun as was described in the third Experiment. By turning the Prism ABC slowly to and fro about its Axis, this Image will be made to move up and down the Board *de*, and by this means all its parts from one end to the other may be made to pass successively through the hole *g* which is made in the middle of that Board. In the mean while another Prism *abc* is to be fixed next after that hole *g*, to refract the trajected Light a second time. And these things being thus ordered, I marked the places M and N of the opposite Wall upon which the refracted Light fell, and found that whilst the two Boards and second Prism remained unmoved, those places by turning the first Prism about its Axis were changed perpetually. For when the lower part of the Light which fell upon the second Board *de* was cast through the hole *g*, it went to a lower place M on the Wall and when the higher part of that Light was cast through the same hole *g*, it went to a higher place N on the Wall, and when any intermediate part of the Light was cast through that hole, it went to some place on the Wall between M and N. The unchanged Position of the holes in the Boards, made the Incidence of the Rays upon the second Prism to be the same in all cases. And yet in that common Incidence some of the Rays were more refracted, and others less. And those were more refracted in this Prism, which by a greater Refraction in the first Prism were more turned out of the way, and therefore for their Constancy of being more refracted are deservedly called more refrangible.

Chapter 9: Scientific academies across Europe

9.1 'Introduction to the *Saggi* of the Accademia del Cimento', 1667; reproduced in W. E. K. Middleton, *The Experimenters: A Study of the Accademia del Cimento*, 1971. London: Johns Hopkins University Press

TO THE MOST SERENE FERDINAND II, GRAND DUKE OF TUSCANY

MOST SERENE LORD:

The printing of the first samples of the experiments in natural philosophy that have been made for many years in our Academy with the assistance and under the continued protection of the Most Serene Prince Leopold Your Highness' brother, will itself carry to those regions of the world in which virtue shines most brightly, new evidence of the great munificence of Your Highness and call back towards you with a new sense of gratitude the true lovers of the fine arts and the most noble sciences. We ourselves are the more greatly moved to a more devoted acknowledgment, for we have been so much nearer, enjoying the strong influence of your beneficent hand. Meanwhile, with the favor of your protection, with the stimulus of your ability and your own taste and inclination, and above all with the honor of your presence, sometimes coming into the Academy and sometimes calling it into your Royal apartments, you have given the Academy its reputation and its fervor and at the same time enlarged the progress of our studies.

These considerations very easily teach us our clear duty of consecrating to Your Highness' lofty name this first fruit of our labors, inasmuch as nothing can come from us in which Your Highness might have a greater part and which it would thus be more proper to offer you or which would come nearer to meriting the good fortune of your generous approval. Truly, for the superabundance of so many and so remarkable favors we feel no greater desire than to see ourselves thus strictly bound to Your Highness; not because we willingly carry the burden of such precious and valued obligations, but because we should wish only to be able to offer you something that is not your own, so that we might at least flatter ourselves that we had brought you some slight recompense and expressed some thanks of our own choice to Your Highness that would not be entirely your own or from necessity. But now we are perforce content to have in our hearts such just and proper sentiments, since the fruit of these new philosophical speculations is so strongly rooted in Your Highness' protection that not only what our Academy produces today but everything that matures in the most famous schools of Europe, and that will come to light in succeeding ages, will likewise properly be due to Your Highness as the gift of your beneficence. For as long as sun, stars, and planets shine and the heavens endure, there will remain the glorious memory of one who contributed so much with the power of his most happy favors to such new and stupendous discoveries and to the opening of an untrodden path to the more exact investigation of truth. Although we have so little to offer, there is something that sharpens our respectful gratitude. This indeed is the pleasure with which we bear our poverty, while everything overflows in the greater abundance of glory for Your Highness, who, having yourself done whatever new, good, and great things will ever be found in the wealth of the sciences, have enfeebled in others all power to equal you. So much and no more are we in a position to offer Your Highness. Filled with reverence and homage and begging your continued protection, we pray God to grant you the highest prosperity and greatness.

Your Highness' very humble servants,

THE ACADEMICIANS OF THE CIMENTO

Florence, 14 July 1667
The Secretary for the *Saggi*

[. . .]

Preface

Without any doubt the first born of all the creatures of the Divine wisdom was the idea of Truth, to which the eternal Architect held so closely in his plan for the building of the universe that nothing whatever was made with even the slightest alloy of falsehood. But when later on, in the contemplation of such a high and perfect structure, man acquired too immoderate a desire to understand the marvellous power of it and to take the measure and proportions of such a beautiful harmony, then, wishing to enter too completely into the truth, he came to create an indefinite number of falsehoods. This had no other cause but the desire for those wings that Nature did not want to give him, perhaps fearing that she might at some time be surprised in the preparation of her most stupendous works. On such wings he began to soar, though oppressed by the weight of his material body, gaining the strength to rise higher than the gamut of perceptible things, and so tried to fix himself in a light such as is no longer light when it enters the eyes, but, fading, darkens and changes color.

This was how the first seeds of false opinions arose from human rashness. It is not that the brightness of God's beautiful creations is at all obscured by this, or that they are in any way spoilt by their commerce with it; for these defects all lie in human ignorance, where they have their root. Meanwhile, man, improperly fitting causes to effects, takes their true essence neither from one nor the other, but putting them together forms a false science within his own mind. But it is not that the sovereign beneficence of God, when creating our souls, does not let them glance for an instant, so to speak, at the immense treasure of His eternal wisdom, adorning them with the first gleams of truth as with precious gems. We see that this is true from the notions, preserved in our spirits, that we cannot have learned here, but must inevitably have gathered from another place.

But it is indeed our misfortune that these most noble jewels, badly held in the setting of a soul still too tender, just as it comes down into its earthly house and wraps itself in this common clay, at once fall out of their fastenings and are so befouled as to be worthless, until at length by assiduous and eager study they are brought back to their places. Now this is exactly what the soul is trying to do in the investigation of natural things. [. . .] Now here, where we are no longer permitted to step forward, there is nothing better to turn to than our faith in experiment. As one may take a heap of loose and unset jewels and seek to put them back one after another into their setting, so experiment, fitting effects to causes and causes to effects—though it may not succeed at the first throw, like Geometry—performs enough so that by trial and error it sometimes succeeds in hitting the target.

But we must proceed with great caution lest too much faith in experiment should deceive us, since before it shows us manifest truth, after lifting the first veils of more evident falsehood, it always makes visible certain misleading appearances that seem to be true. These are those indistinct outlines that show through the last veils that cover the lovely image of Truth more closely, through the fineness of which she sometimes appears so vividly pictured that anyone might say that all was discovered. Here, then, it is our business to have a masterly understanding of the ways of truth and falsehood and to use our own judgment as shrewdly as we can, so as to see clearly whether it is or is not. There is no doubt that to be able to do better we must at some time have seen Truth unveiled, an advantage possessed only by those who have acquired some taste for the study of geometry.

Yet besides trying new experiments, it is not less useful to search among those already made, in case any might be found that might in any way have counterfeited the pure face of Truth. So it has been the aim of our Academy, besides doing whatever experiments occurred to us, to make them, either from fruitful curiosity or for comparison, on those things that have been done or written about by others, as unfortunately we see errors being established by things that go by the name of experiments. This was precisely what first moved the most perspicaceous and indefatigable mind of His Highness Prince Leopold of Tuscany, who, as a recreation after the diligent management of affairs and the ceaseless anxieties that arise from his exalted state, began to exercise his intellect upon the steep road of the most noble kinds of knowledge. Therefore it was quite easy for His Highness' sublime understanding to see how the trust in great authors is most often inimical to talented men. Either from excessive trust or from reverence for a name, such people dare not consider doubtful what is conjectured on such great authority. His Highness decided that it should be the task of his great spirit to verify the value of their assertions by wiser and more exact experiments: and when the proof or the refutation had been obtained, to present it as a gift, so precious and so desirable, to whomsoever is anxious to discover Truth.

These prudent precepts of His Highness our protector, embraced by the Academy with the veneration and esteem that they deserved, have not had it as their aim to make them indiscreet censors of other laborious scholars, or presumptuous dispensers of truth or error; but have mainly been intended to encourage other people to repeat the same experiments with the greatest rigor, just as we have sometimes dared to do to those of others, even though in publishing these first examples we have for the most part abstained from this, the better to confirm, with proper regards to all our readers, the sincerity of our dispassionate and respectful opinions. In fact, to give full scope to such a noble and useful enterprise we should wish for nothing else but a free communication from the various Societies, scattered as they are today throughout the most illustrious and notable region of Europe. These, opening such a profitable mutual correspondence with the same purpose of reaching such important ends, would all go on searching with the same liberty, according to their means, and participating in Truth. For our part, we shall contribute to this work with the greatest sincerity and ingenuousness.

Wherever we have reported the experiments of others, we have always cited the authors, as far as they were known to us, and have often freely confessed being much helped in these trials, which we did not after all succeed in bringing to as happy an end. But as the clearest proof of the open sincerity of our procedure, all may see the liberality with which we have always shared them with anyone passing through these parts who showed a desire to enjoy some account of them, whether as an act of courtesy, or because he esteemed learning, or from the incentive of noble curiosity. This we have done since the first days of our Academy, founded in the year 1657, during which early days were discovered, if not all, then the greater part of the things of which these examples are now being printed.

If, after all, someone perceives that among the things that we give out as ours some are to be found that were first imagined and published by others, this will never be our fault; for as we can neither know all nor see all, nobody should marvel at the correspondence between our intellects and those of others, just as we really are not surprised at the correspondence between theirs and ours.

We should certainly not wish anyone to persuade himself that we have the presumption to bring out a finished work, or even a perfect pattern of a great experimental history, knowing well that more time and labor are going to be required for such a purpose. Everyone may perceive this from the very title we have given this book, merely of examples. We should never even have published this without the powerful stimulus that we have had from honorable people whose kind entreaties persuaded us to suffer the shame of printing such imperfect beginnings.

Finally, before everything else we protest that we would never wish to pick a quarrel with anyone, entering into subtle disputes or vain contradictions; and if sometimes in passing from one experiment to another, or for any other reason whatever, some slight hint of speculation is given, this is always to be taken as the opinion or private sentiment of the academicians, never that of the Academy, whose only task is to make experiments and to tell about them. For such was our first intention and also the purpose of that exalted Person who with his particular protection and great knowledge led us along the way, and whose wise and prudent counsel we have always exactly and regularly obeyed.

9.2 'On the History of the Royal Society: The Preface and Design of this Discourse', from Thomas Sprat, *History of the Royal Society*, 1667. London: RKP reprint, 1966, pp. 1–3

THE
HISTORY
OF THE
Institution, Design, and *Progress*
OF THE
ROYAL SOCIETY
OF
LONDON.

For the Advancement of Experimental Philosophy.

THE FIRST PART

I shall here present to the World, an Account of the *First Institution* of the *Royal Society;* and of the *Progress,* which they have already made: in hope, that this Learned and Inquisitive Age, will either think their Indeavours, worthy of its *Assistance;* or else will be thereby provok'd, to attempt some *greater Enterprise* (if any such can be found out) for the Benefit of humane life, by the Advancement of *Real Knowledge.* [. . .] For what greater matter can any man desire, about which to employ his thoughts, then the Beginnings of an *Illustrious Company,* which has already laid such excellent Foundations of so much good to *Mankind?* Or, what can be more delightful for an *Englishman* to consider, then that notwithstanding all the late miseries of his Country; it has been able in a short time so well to recover itself: as not onely to attain to the perfection of its *former* Civility, and Learning, but also to set on foot, a *new* way of improvement of

Arts, as *Great* and as *Beneficial* (to say no more) as any the wittiest or the happiest Age has ever invented?

But besides this, I can also add, in my Defence, that though the *Society*, of which I am to write, is not yet four years old, and has been of necessity hitherto chiefly taken up, about *Preparatory Affairs*: yet even in this time, they have not wholly neglected their *principal End*; but have had Success, in the tryal of many remarkable things; of which I doubt not, but I shall be able, as I pass along, to give instances enough to satisfie the curiosity of all *Sober Inquirers* into Truth. And in short, if for no other end, yet certainly for this, A Relation of their First Original ought to be expos'd to the view of Men: that by laying down, on what course of Discovery they intend to proceed, the *Gentlemen of the Society*, may be more solemnly engag'd to *prosecute* the same. For now they will not be able, handsomely to draw back, and to forsake such honourable Intentions: when the World shall have taken notice, that so many prudent men have gone so farr, in a business of this Universal Importance, and have given such undoubted *Pledges*, of many admirable Inventions to follow.

9.3 'On the History of the Royal Society: A Model of their Whole Design', from Thomas Sprat, *History of the Royal Society*, 1667. London: RKP reprint, 1966, pp. 61–76

Their purpose is, in short, to make faithful *Records*, of all the Works of *Nature*, or *Art*, which can come within their reach: that so the present Age, and posterity, may be able to put a mark on the Errors, which have been strengthened by long prescription: to restore the Truths, that have lain neglected: to push on those, which are already known, to more various uses: and to make the way more passable, to what remains unreveal'd. This is the compass of their Design. And to accomplish this, they have indeavor'd, to separate the knowledge of *Nature*, from the colours of *Rhetorick*, the devices of *Fancy*, or the delightful deceit of *Fables*. They have labor'd to inlarge it, from being confin'd to the custody of a few, or from servitude to private interests. They have striven to preserve it from being over-press'd by a confus'd heap of vain, and useless particulars; or from being straitned and bounded too much up by General Doctrines. They have try'd, to put it into a condition of perpetual increasing; by settling an inviolable correspondence between the hand, and the brain. They have studi'd, to make it, not onely an Enterprise of one season, or of some lucky opportunity; but a business of time; a steddy, a lasting, a popular, an uninterrupted Work. They have attempted, to free it from the Artifice, and Humors, and Passions of Sects; to render it an Instrument, whereby Mankind may obtain a Dominion over *Things*, and not onely over one anothers *Judgements*. And lastly, they have begun to establish these Reformations in Philosophy, not so much, by any solemnity of Laws, or ostentation of Ceremonies; as by solid Practice, and examples: not, by a glorious pomp of Words; but by the silent, effectual, and unanswerable Arguments of real Productions. [. . .]

As for what belongs to the *Members* themselves, that are to constitute the *Society*: It is to be noted, that they have freely admitted Men of different Religions, Countries, and Professions of Life. [. . .]

That the *Church of England* ought not to be apprehensive, of this free converse of various Judgments, I shall afterwards manifest at large. For the present, I shall franckly assert; that our *Doctrine*, and *Discipline*, will be so far from receiving damage by it; that it were the best way to make them universally embrac'd, if they were oftner brought to be canvas'd amidst all sorts of dissenters. [. . .]

By their *naturalizing* Men of all Countries, they have laid the beginnings of many great advantages for the future. For by this means, they will be able, to settle a *constant Intelligence*, throughout all civil Nations; and make the *Royal Society* the general *Banck*, and Free-port of the World: A policy, which whether it would hold good, in the *Trade* of *England*, I know not: but sure it will in the *Philosophy*. We are to overcome the mysteries of all the Works of Nature; and not onely to prosecute such as are confin'd to one Kingdom, or beat upon one shore. [. . .]

By their admission of Men of all *professions*, these *two* Benefits arise: The one, that every Art, and every way of life already establish'd, may be secure of receiving no damage by their Counsels. A thing which all new Inventions ought carefully to consult. It is in vain, to declare against the profit of the most, in any change that we would make. [. . .] But the other benefit is, that by this equal Balance of all Professions, there will no one particular of them overweigh the other, or make the *Oracle* onely speak their *private* fence: which else it were impossible to avoid. [. . .]

But, though the *Society* entertains very many men of *particular Professions*; yet the farr greater Number are *Gentlemen*, free, and unconfin'd. By the help of this, there was hopefull Provision made against *two corruptions* of Learning, which have been long complain'd of, but never remov'd: The *one*, that *Knowledge* still degenerates, to consult *present profit* too soon; the *other*, that *Philosophers* have bin always *Masters*, & *Scholars*; some imposing, & all the other submitting; and not as equal observers without dependence. [. . .]

The second Error, wich is hereby endeavour'd to be remedied, is, that the Seats of Knowledg, have been for the most part heretofore, not *Laboratories*, as they ought to be; but onely *Scholes*, where some have *taught*, and all the rest subscrib'd. The consequences of this are very mischievous. [. . .] The very inequality of the Titles of *Teachers*, and *Scholars*, does very much suppress, and tame mens Spirits; which though it should be proper for Discipline and Education; yet is by no means consistent with a free Philosophical Consultation. [. . .]

These therefore are the *Qualities*, which they have principally requir'd, in those, whom they admitted: still reserving to themselves a power of *increasing*, or keeping to their number, as they saw occasion. By this means, they have given assurance of an eternal quietness, and moderation, in their experimental progress; because they allow themselves to differ in the weightiest matter, even in the *way of Salvation* itself. By this they have taken care, that nothing shall be so remote, as to escape their reach: because some of their *Members* are still scattered abroad, in most of the habitable parts of the Earth. By this, they have provided, that no profitable thing shall seem too mean for their consideration, seeing they have some amongst them, whose life is employ'd about *little* things, as well as *great*. By this they have broken down the partition wall, and made a fair entrance, for *all conditions of men* to engage in these Studies; which were heretofore affrighted from them, by a groundless apprehension of their chargeableness, and difficulty. Thus they have form'd that *Society*, which intends a *Philosophy*, for the use of *Cities*, and not for the retirements of *Schools*, to resemble the *Cities* themselves: which are compounded of all sorts of men, of the *Gown*, of the *Sword*, of the *Shop*, of the *Field*, of the *Court*, of the Sea; all mutually assisting each other.

9.4 'On the History of the Royal Society: Their Course of Inquiry', from Thomas Sprat, *History of the Royal Society*, 1667. London: RKP reprint, 1966, pp. 76–100

Let us next consider what *course of Inquiry* they take, to make all their Labours unite for the service of man-kind: And here I shall insist on their *Expence*, their *Instruments*, their *Matter*, and their *Method*.

Of the Stock, upon which their Expence has been hitherto defraid, I can say nothing, that is very *magnificent*: seeing they have rely'd upon no more than some small *Admission-money*, and *weekly Contributions* amongst themselves. Such a *Revenue* as this, can make no great sound, nor amount to any *vast summ*. But yet, I shall say this for it, that it was the onely way, which could have been begun, with a security of success, in that condition of things. The *publick Faith* of *Experimental Philosophy*, was not then strong enough, to move Men and Women of all conditions, to bring in their Bracelets and Jewels, towards the carrying of it on. Such affections as those may be rais'd by a mis-guided zeal; but seldom, or never, by calm and unpassionate Reason. It was therefore well ordain'd, that the first Benevolence should come from the *Experimenters themselves*. If they had speedily at first call'd for *mighty Treasures*; and said aloud, that their Enterprise requir'd the *Exchequer of a Kingdom*; they would onely have been contemn'd, as vain *Projectors*. So ready is man-kind, to suspect all new undertakings to be Cheats, and *Chimæraes*; especialy, when they seem *chargeable*: [. . .]

The suspicion, which is so natural to mens breasts, [. . .] could not any way harm the *Royal Societies* establishment: seeing its first claims, and pretensions were so modest. And yet I shall presume to assure the World; that what they shall raise on these mean Foundations, will be more answerable to the largeness of their intentions, than to the *narrowness* of their beginnings. [. . .] To evidence this; I think it may be calculated, that since the *Kings* Return, there have been more *Acts* of *Parliament*, for the *clearing* and *beautifying* of Streets, for the *repayring* of *Highwayes*, for the *cutting* of *Rivers*, for the *increase* of *Manufactures*, for the setting on foot the Trade of Fishing, and many other such Publick Works, to adorn the State; than in divers Ages before. This *General Temper* being well weigh'd; it cannot be imagin'd, that the *Nation* will withdraw its assistance from the *Royal Society* alone; which does not intend to stop at some *particular benefit*, but goes to the root of *all noble Inventions*, and proposes an infallible course to make *England* the glory of the Western world. [. . .]

In their *Method of Inquiring*, I will observe, how they have behav'd themselves, in things that might be brought within their *own Touch and Sight*: and how in those, which are so remote, and hard to be come by, that about them, they were forc'd to trust *the reports of others*.

In the first kind: I shall lay it down, as their *Fundamental Law*, that whenever they could possibly get to *handle* the subject, the *Experiment* was still perform'd by some of the *Members* themselves. [. . .] And the Task was divided amongst them, by one of these two ways. First, it was sometimes referr'd to some *particular men*, to make choice of what *Subject* they pleased, and to follow their own humour in the *Trial*; the *expence* being still allow'd from the general Stock. [. . .]

Or else secondly, the *Society* it self made the distribution, and deputed whom it thought fit for the prosecution of such, or such Experiments. And this they did, either by allotting the *same Work* to *several* men, separated one from another; or else by *joyning* them into *Committees*. [. . .] By this *union of eyes*, and *hands* there do these *advantages* arise. Thereby there will be a full *comprehension* of the object in *all* its appearances; and so there will be a mutual communication of the light of one *Science* to another: whereas *single labours* can be but as a prospect taken upon one side. And also by this fixing of several mens thoughts upon one thing, there will be an excellent cure for that *defect*, which is almost unavoidable in great *Inventors*. It is the custom of such earnest, and powerful minds, to do wonderful things in the *beginning*; but shortly after, to be overborn by the multitude, and weight of their own thoughts; then to yield, and cool by little and little; and at last grow weary, and even to loath that, upon which they were at first the most eager. [. . .]

For this, the best provision must be, to join many men together; for it cannot be imagin'd, that they should be all so violent, and fiery: and so by this mingling of *Tempers*, the *Impetuous* men, not having the whole burthen on them, may have leisure for intervals to recruit their first heat; and the more *judicious*, who are not so soon possess'd with such raptures, may carry on the others strong conceptions, by soberer degrees, to a full accomplishment.

This they have practis'd in such things, whereof the matter is common; and wherein they may repeat their labours as they please. But in *forein*, and *remote* affairs, their *Intentions*, and their *Advantages* do farr exceed all others. For these, they have begun to settle a *correspondence* through all Countreys; and have taken such order, that in short time, there will scarce a Ship come up the *Thames*, that does not make some return of *Experiments*, as well as of *Merchandize*.

This their care of an *Universal Intelligence*, is befriended by *Nature* its self, in the situation of *England*: For, lying so, as it does, in the passage between the Northern parts of the World, and the *Southern*; its *Ports* being open to all Coasts, and its *Ships* spreading their Sails in all Seas; it is thereby necessarily made, not onely *Mistress* of the *Ocean*, but the most proper *Seat*, for the advancement of *Knowledg*. From the *positions* of Countreys, arise not only their several shapes, manners, customs, colours, but also their *different Arts*, and *Studies*. The *Inland* and *Continent*, we see do give Laws, to Discourse, to Habits, to Behaviour: but those that border upon the *Seas*, are most properly seated, to bring home matter for *new Sciences*, and to make the same proportion of Discoveries above others, in the *Intellectual* Globe, as they have done in the *Material*. [. . .]

Their *Matter*, being thus collected, has been brought before their *weekly meetings*, to undergo a just and a full examination. In them their principal endeavours have been, that they might enjoy the benefits of a *mix'd Assembly*, which are largeness of Observation, and diversity of Judgments, without the mischiefs that usually accompany it, such as confusion, unsteddiness, and the little animosities of divided Parties. That they have avoided these dangers for the time past; there can be no better proof, than their constant practice; wherein they have perpetually preserv'd a singular sobriety of debating, slowness of consenting, and moderation of dissenting. Nor have they been onely free from *Faction*, but from the very *Causes*, and *beginnings* of it. It was in vain for any man amongst them to strive to preferr himself before another; or to seek for any great glory from the subtilty of his Wit; seeing it was the inartificial process of the *Experiment*, and not the *Acuteness* of any Commentary upon it, which they have had in veneration. There was no room left, for any to attempt, to heat their own, or others minds, beyond a due temper; where they were not allow'd to expatiate, or amplifie, or connect specious arguments together. [. . .]

Towards the first of these ends, it has been their usual course, when they themselves appointed the *Trial*, to propose one week, some particular *Experiments*, to be prosecuted the next; and to debate beforehand, concerning all things that might conduce to the better carrying them on. In this *Præliminary Collection*, it has been the custom, for any of the *Society*, to urge what came into their thoughts, or memories concerning them; either from the observations of others, or from *Books*, or from their own *Experience*, or even from common *Fame* it self. And in performing this, they did not exercise any great rigour of choosing, and distinguishing between *Truths* and *Falshoods*: but a mass altogether as they came; the certain Works, the Opinions, the Ghesses, the Inventions, with their different Degrees and Accidents, the Probabilities, and Problems, the general Conceptions, the miraculous Stories, the ordinary Productions, the changes incident to the same Matter in several places, the Hindrances, the Benefits, of *Airs*, or *Seasons*, or *Instruments*; and whatever they found to have been begun, to have fail'd, to have succeeded, in the Matter which was then under their Disquisition.

This is a most necessary preparation, to any that resolve to make a perfect search. For they cannot but go blindly, and lamely, and confusedly about the business, unless they have first laid before them a full *Account* of it. [. . .]

Those, to whom the conduct of the *Experiment* is committed, being dismiss'd with these advantages, do (as it were) carry the eyes, and the imaginations of the whole company into the *Laboratory* with them. And after they have perform'd the *Trial*, they bring all the *History* of its *process* back again to the *test*. Then comes in the second great Work of the *Assembly*; which is to *judg*, and *resolve* upon the matter of *Fact*. In this part of their imployment, they us'd to take an exact view of the repetition of the whole course of the *Experiment*; here they observ'd all the *chances*, and the *Regularities* of the proceeding; what *Nature* does willingly, what constrain'd; what with its own power, what by the succours of Art; what in a constant rode, and what with some kind of sport and extravagance; industriously marking all the various shapes into which it turns it self, when it is persued, and by how many secret passages it at last obtains its end; never giving it over till the whole *Company* has been fully satisfi'd of the certainty and constancy; or, on the otherside, of the absolute impossibility of the effect. This *critical*, and *reiterated scrutiny* of those things, which are the plain objects of their eyes; must needs put out of all reasonable dispute, the reality of those operations, which the *Society* shall positively determine to have succeeded. If any shall still think it a just *Philosophical liberty*, to be jealous of resting on their credit: they are in the right; and their *dissentings* will be most thankfully receiv'd, if they be establish'd on solid works, and not onely on *prejudices*, or *suspicions*. To the *Royal Society* it will be at any time almost as acceptable, to be *confuted*, as to *discover*: seeing, by this means, they will accomplish their main *Design*: others will be inflam'd: many more will labour; and so the *Truth* will be obtain'd between them: which may be as much promoted by the *contentions* of hands, and eyes; as it is commonly injur'd by those of Tongues. However, that men may not hence undervalue their *authority*, because they themselves are not willing to impose, and to usurp a *dominion* over their reason; I will tell them, that there is not any one thing, which is now approv'd and practis'd in the World, that is confirm'd by stronger evidence, than this, which the *Society* requires; except onely the *Holy Mysteries of our Religion*. In almost all other matters of *Belief*, of *Opinion*, or of *Science*; the assurance, whereby men are guided, is nothing near so firm as this.

Chapter 10: The reception of Newtonianism in Europe

10.1 W. J. 'sGravesande, *Mathematical Elements of Natural Philosophy*, 3rd edn., 1726. London

The Study of Natural Philosophy is not however to be contemned, as built upon an unknown Foundation. The Sphere of humane Knowledge is bounded within a narrow Compass; and he, that denies his Assent to every Thing but Evidence, wavers in Doubt every Minute; and looks upon many Things as unknown which the Generality of People never so much as call in Question. But rightly to distinguish Things known, from Things unknown, is a Perfection above the Level of human Mind. Though many Things in Nature are hidden from us; yet what is set down in Physics, as a Science, is undoubted. From a few general Principles numberless particular Phænomena or Effects are explained, and deduced by Mathematical Demonstration. For, the comparing of Motion, or in other Words, of Quantities, is the continual Theme; and whoever will go about that Work any other Way, than by Mathematical Demonstrations, will be sure to fall into Uncertainties at least, if not in Errors.

How much soever then may be unknown in Natural Philosophy, it still remains a vast, certain and very useful Science. It corrects an infinite Number of Prejudices concerning natural Things, and divine Wisdom; and, as we examine the Works of GOD continually, sets that Wisdom before our Eyes; and there is a wide Difference, betwixt knowing the divine Power and Wisdom by a Metaphysical Argument, and beholding them with our Eyes every Minute in their Effects. It appears then sufficiently, what is the End of Physics, from what Laws of Nature the Phænomena are to be deduced, and wherefore, when we are once come to the general Laws, we cannot penetrate any further into the Knowledge of Causes. There remains only to discourse of the Method of searching after those Laws; and to prove that the three *Newtonian* Laws delivered in the first Chapter of this Work ought to be followed.

The first is, *That we ought not to admit any more Causes of Natural Things, than what are true, and sufficient to explain their Phænomena.* The first Part of this Rule plainly follows from what has been said above. The other cannot be called in Question by any that owns the Wisdom of the Creator. If one Cause suffices, it is needless to superadd another; especially, if it be considered, that an Effect from a double Cause is never exactly the same with an Effect from a single one. Therefore we are not to multiply Causes, till it appears one single Cause will not do the Business.

In order to prove the following Rules, we must premise some general Reflections.

We have already said, that Mathematical Demonstrations have no Standard to be judged by, but their Conformity with our Ideas; and when the Question is

Mathematical
ELEMENTS
OF
Natural Philofophy,

Confirm'd by EXPERIMENTS;

OR, AN

INTRODUCTION
TO

Sir ISAAC NEWTON's Philofophy.

VOL. I.

Written in LATIN,

By WILLIAM-JAMES 'sGRAVESANDE, Doctor of Laws and Philofophy, Profeffor of Mathematicks and Aftronomy at *Leyden*, and Fellow of the Royal Society of *London*.

Tranflated into ENGLISH,

By *J. T. Defaguliers*, LL. D. Fellow of the Royal Society, and Chaplain to his Grace the Duke of CHANDOS.

The Third EDITION.

LONDON:

Printed for J. SENEX in *Fleetftreet*, W. and J. INNYS, in St. *Paul's* Churchyard; and J. OSBORN and T. LONGMAN, in *Pater-Nofter-Row*.

M DCC XXVI

about Natural Things, the first Requisite is, that our Ideas agree with those Things, which cannot be proved by any Mathematical Demonstration. And yet as we have Occasion to reason of Things themselves every Moment, and of those Things nothing can be present to our Minds besides our Ideas, upon which our Reasonings immediately turn; it follows, that God has established some Rules, by which we may judge of the Agreement of our Ideas with the Things themselves.

All Mathematical Reasonings turn upon the Comparison of Quantities, and their Truth is evidenc'd by implying a Contradiction in a contrary Proposition. A rectilineal Triangle, for Instance, whose three Angles are not equal to two right ones, is a Thing impossible. When the Question is not about the Comparison of Quantities, a contrary Proposition is not always impossible. It is certain, for Instance, that *Peter* is living, though it is as certain that he might have died Yesterday. Now there being numberless Cases of that Kind, where one may affirm or deny with equal Certainty; there follows, that there are many Reasonings very certain, tho' altogether different from the Mathematical Ones. And they evidently follow from the Establishment of Things, and therefore from the pre-determined Will of God. For by forcing Men upon the Necessity of pronouncing concerning the Truth or Falshood of a Proposition; he plainly shews they must assent to Agreements, which their Judgments necessarily acquiesce in; and whoever reasons otherwise, does not think worthily of God.

To return to *Physics*; we are in this Science to judge by our Senses, of the Agreement that there is betwixt Things and our Ideas. The Extension and Solidity of Matter, for Instance, asserted upon that Ground, are past all Doubt. Here we examine the Thing in general, without taking notice of the Fallacy of our Senses upon some Occasions, and which Way Error is then to be avoided.

We cannot immediately judge of all Physical Matters by our Senses. We have then Recourse to another just Way of reasoning, though not Mathematical. It depends upon this Axiom; (viz.) *We must look upon as true, whatever being denied would destroy civil Society, and deprive us of the Means of Living.* From which Proposition the second and third Rules of the *Newtonian* Method most evidently follow.

For who could live a Minute's Time in Tranquility, if a Man was to doubt the Truth of what passes for certain, wherever Experiments have been made about it; and if he did not depend upon seeing the like Effects produced by the same Cause?

The following Reasonings, for Example, are daily taken for granted as undoubtedly true, without any previous Examination; because every Body sees that they cannot be called in Question without destroying the present Œconomy of Nature.

A Building, this Day firm in all its Parts, will not of itself run to Ruin to Morrow. Thus, by a Parity of Reason, the Cohesion and Gravity of the Parts of Bodies, which I never saw altered, nor heard of having been altered, without some intervening external Cause, will not be altered to Night, because the Cause of Cohesion and Gravity will be the same to Morrow as it is to Day. Who does not see, that the Certainty of this Reasoning depends only upon the Truth of the fore-mentioned Principle?

The Timber and Stones of any Country, which are fit for a Building, if brought over here, will serve in this Place, except what Changes may arise from an external Cause; and I shall no more fear the Fall of my Building, than the Inhabitants of the Country, from whence those Materials were brought, wou'd do, if they had built a House with them. Thus the Power which causes the Cohesion of Parts, and that which gives Weight to Bodies, are the same in all Countries.

I have used such Kind of Food for so many Years, therefore I will use it again to Day without Fear.

When I see Hemlock, I conclude it to be poisonous, tho' I never made an Experiment of that very Hemlock I see before my Eyes.

All these Reasonings are grounded upon Analogy; and there is no Doubt, but our Creator has in many Cases left us no other Way of Reasoning, and therefore it is a right Way.

Which being once prov'd, we may afterwards make use of the same Method in other Matters, where no absolute Necessity forces us to reason at all. When an Argument is good in one Case, there is no Reason why we should refuse our Assent to it in another. For who can conceive, that Things proved the same Way are not equally certain? Besides, tho' we conclude in general, that this Method of Reasoning is right from the Necessity of using it; yet it does not follow that particular Reasonings depend upon that Necessity. I conclude from Analogy, that Food is not poisonous; but is that Argument only good, when I am hungry?

In Physics then we are to discover the Laws of Nature by the Phænomena, then by Induction prove them to be general Laws; all the rest is to be handled Mathematically. Whoever will seriously examine, what Foundation this Method Physics is built upon, will easily discover this to be the only true one, and that all Hypotheses are to be laid aside.

So much for the Method of philosophising. I have now a Word to say of the Work itself, of which this is the first Tome.

The whole Work is divided into four Books. The first treats of Body in general, and the Motion of Solid Bodies. The Second of Fluids. What belongs to Light is handled in the Third. The Fourth explains the motions of Celestial Bodies, and what has a Relation to them upon Earth. The two first Books are contained in this Tome.

In Order to render the Study of Natural Philosophy as easy and agreeable as possible, I have thought fit to illustrate every Thing by Experiments, and to set the very Mathematical Conclusions before the Reader's Eyes by this Method.

He, that sets forth the Elements of a Science, does not promise the learned World any Thing new in the main. Therefore I thought it needless, to point out where what is here contained is to be found. I have made my Property of whatever served my Purpose; and I thought giving Notice of it, once for all, was sufficient to avoid the Suspicion of Theft. I had rather lose the Honour of a few Discoveries, dispersed here and there in this Treatise, than rob any one of theirs. Let who will then take to himself what he thinks his own: I lay claim to nothing.

As to Machines which serve for making the Experiments, I have taken care to imitate several from other Authors, have altered and improved others, and added many new ones of my own Invention. And no Wonder I should be forced to that Necessity, having made Experiments upon many Things never tried perhaps by any one before. For Mathematicians think Experiments superfluous, where Mathematical Demonstrations will take Place: But as all Mathematical Demonstrations are abstracted, I do not question their becoming easier, when Experiments set forth the Conclusions before our Eyes; following therein the Example of the *English*, whose Way of teaching Natural Philosophy gave me Occasion to think of the Method I have followed in this Work. I shall always glory in treading in their Footsteps, who, with the Prince of Philosophers for their Guide, have first opened the Way to the Discovery of Truth in Philosophical Matters.

As to the Machines, I will say thus much more by Way of Advertisement, That most of them have been made by a very ingenious Artist of this Town, and no unskilful Philosopher, whose Name is *John van Musschenbroek*, and who has a perfect Knowledge of every Thing that is here explained. Which Advertisement, I suppose, will not be displeasing to those who may have a Fancy to get some of those Machines made for themselves.

10.2 Ephraim Chambers, *Cyclopaedia*, London, 1728

NEWTONIAN *Phylosophy*, the doctrine of the universe, and particularly of the heavenly bodies; their laws, affections, &c. as delivered by Sir Isaac Newton. See PHILSOPHY.

The term *Newtonian Philosophy*, is applied very differently; whence divers confused notions relating thereto.

Some authors, under this philosophy, include all the corpuscular philosophy, considered as it now stands corrected and reformed by the discoveries, and improvements made in several parts thereof, by Sir Isaac Newton.

In which sense it is that Graavesande calls his elements of physics, *Introductio ad Philosophiam* Newtonianam.

And in this sense the *Newtonian* is the same with the new philosophy, and stands contradistinguished to the cartesian, the peripatetic, and the ancient corpuscular. See CORPUSCULAR, PERIPATETIC, CARTESIAN, &c.

Others by *Newtonian Philosophy*, mean the method or order which Sir Isaac Newton observes in philosophizing; *viz.* the reasoning, and drawing of conclusions directly from phænomena, exclusive of all previous hypotheses; the beginning from simple principles, deducing the first powers and laws of nature from a few select phænomena, and then applying those laws, &c. to account for other things. See *Law of* NATURE. And in this sense, the *Newtonian Philosophy* is the same with the experimental philosophy; and stands opposed to the ancient corpuscular. See EXPERIMENTAL, &c.

Others, by *Newtonian Philosophy*, mean that wherein physical bodies are considered mathematically; and where geometry, and mechanics are applied to the solution of phænomena.

In which sense, the *Newtonian* is the same with the mechanical, and mathematical philosophy. See MECHANICAL.

Others, again, by *Newtonian Philosophy*, understand that part of physical knowledge, which Sir Isaac Newton has handled, improved, and demonstrated, in his *Principia*.

Others, lastly, by *Newtonian Philosophy*, mean, the new principles which Sir Isaac Newton has brought into philosophy, the new system founded thereon; and the new solutions of phænomena thence deduced; or that which characterizes, and distinguishes his philosophy from all others.—Which is the sense wherein we shall chiefly consider it.

As to the history of this philosophy we have but little to say: It was first made public in the year 1686, by the author, then a fellow of Trinity-college, Cambridge; and in the year 1713, republished with considerable improvements.— Several other authors have since attempted to make it plainer; by setting aside many of the more sublime mathematical researches, and substituting either more obvious reasonings, or experiments, in lieu thereof; particularly Whiston in his *Prælect. Phys. Mathemat.* Gravesande in *Element. & Instit.* and Dr. Pemberton in his *View*.

Notwithstanding the great merit of this philosophy, and the universal reception it has met with at home, it gains ground very slowly abroad; *Newtonianism* has scarce two or three adherents in a nation; but *Cartesianism, Huygenianism*, and *Leibnitzianism* remain still in the chief possession.

The *Philosophy* itself is laid down principally in the third book of the *Principia*. The two preceding books are taken up in the preparing the way, and laying down such principles of mathematicks as have the most relation to philosophy: Such are the laws and conditions of powers. And these, to render them less dry and geometrical, the author illustrates by scholia in philosophy, relating chiefly to the density and resistance of bodies, the motion of light, and sounds, a vacuum, &c.

In the third book he proceeds to the *Philosophy* itself; and from the same principles deduces the structure of the universe, and the powers of gravity, whereby bodies tend towards the sun and planets; and from these powers, the motions of the planets and comets, the theory of the moon and tides.

This book, which he calls *de Mundi Systemate,* he tells us, was first wrote in the popular way: But considering, that such as are unacquainted with the said principles, would not conceive the force of the consequences, nor be induced to lay aside their ancient prejudices; for this reason, and to prevent the thing from being in continual dispute; he digested the sum of that book into propositions, in the mathematical manner; so as it might only come to be read by such as had first considered the principles. Not that it is necessary, a man should master them all. Many of them, even the first-rate mathematicians, would find a difficulty in getting over. It is enough to have read the definitions, laws of motion, and the three first sections of the first book; after which, the author himself directs us to pass on to the book *de Systemate Mundi.*

The several articles of this *Philosophy,* are delivered under their respective heads in this dictionary; as Sun, Moon, Planet, Comet, Earth, Air, Centrifugal *Force,* Resistance, Medium, Matter, Space, Elasticity, &c. A general idea, or abstract of the whole, we shall here gratify the reader withal; to shew in what relation the several parts stand to each other.

The great principle on which the whole philosophy is founded, is the power of gravity. This principle is not new: Kepler, long ago, hinted it in his *Introduct. ad Mot. Martis.* He even discovered some of the properties thereof, and their effects in the motions of the primary planets: But the glory of bringing it to a physical demonstration was reserved to the English philosopher. See Gravity.

His proof of the principle from phænomena, together with the application of the same principle to the various other appearances of nature, or the deducing those appearances from that principle, constitute the *Newtonian* system; which, drawn in miniature, will stand thus.

1°. The phænomena are, 1. That the satellites of Jupiter do, by radii drawn to the centre of the planet, describe areas proportional to their times; and that their periodical times are in a sesquiplicate ratio of their distances from its centre: In which all observations of all astronomers agree. 2. The same phænomenon holds of the satellites of Saturn, with regard to Saturn; and of the moon, with regard to the earth. 3. The periodical times of the primary planets about the sun, are in a sesquiplicate ratio of their mean distances from the sun. But, 4. the primary planets do not describe areas any way proportional to their periodical times, about the earth; as being sometimes seen stationary, and sometimes retrograde with regard thereto. See Satellites, Period, &c.

2°. The powers whereby the satellites of Jupiter are constantly drawn out of their rectilinear course, and retained in their orbits, do respect the centre of Jupiter, and are reciprocally as the squares of their distances from the same centre. 2. The same holds of the satellites of Saturn, with regard to Saturn; of the moon with regard to the earth: And of the primary planets with regard to the sun. See Central *Force.*

3°. The moon gravitates towards the earth, and by the power of that gravity is retained in her orbit: And the same holds of the other satellites, with respect to their primary planets; and of the primaries with respect to the sun. See MOON.

As to the moon, the proposition is thus proved: The moon's mean distance is 60 semidiameters of the earth; her period, with regard to the fixed stars, is 27 days, 7 hours, 43 minutes, and the earth's circumference 123249600 Paris feet. Now, supposing the moon to have lost all its motion, and to be let drop to the earth, with the power which retains her in her orbit; in the space of one minute she will fall $15\frac{1}{12}$ Paris feet; the arch she describes in her mean motion at the distance of 60 semidiameters of the earth being the versed sine of $15\frac{1}{12}$ Paris feet. Hence, as the power, as it approaches the earth, increases in a duplicate ratio of the distance inversly; so, as at the surface of the earth, it is 60×60 greater than at the moon: A body falling with that force in our region must, in a minute's time, describe the space of $60 \times 60 \times 15\frac{1}{12}$ Paris feet; and $15\frac{1}{12}$ Paris feet, in the space of one second.

But this is the rate at which bodies fall, by gravity, at the surface of our earth; as Huygens has demonstrated, by experiments with pendulums. Consequently, the power whereby the moon is retained in her orbit, is the same with that we call gravity: For if they were different, a body falling with both powers together, would descend with double the velocity, and in a second of time describes $30\frac{1}{6}$ feet. See DESCENT *of Bodies.*

As to the other secondary planets, their phænomena, with respect to their primary ones, being of the same kind with those of the moon about the earth; it is argued, by analogy, they depend on the same causes: It being a rule or axiom which all philosophers agree to, that effects of the same kind have the same causes. Again, attraction is always mutual, *i.e.* the reaction is equal to the action. Consequently, the primary planets gravitate towards their secondary ones; the earth towards the moon, and sun towards them all. And this gravity, with regard to each several planet, is reciprocally as the square of its distance from its centre of gravity. See ATTRACTION, REACTION, &c.

4°. All bodies gravitate towards all the planets; and their weights towards any one planet, at equal distances from the centre of the planet, are proportional to the quantity of matter in each.

For the law of the descent of heavy bodies towards the earth, setting aside their unequal retardation from the resistance of the air, is this; that all bodies fall equally in equal times: But the nature of gravity or weight, no doubt, is the same on the other planets, as on the earth. See WEIGHT.

Suppose, *e.gr.* such bodies raised to the surface of the moon, and together with the moon deprived at once of all progressive motion, and dropped towards the earth: It is shewn, that in equal times they would describe equal spaces with the moon; and, therefore, that their quantity of matter is to that of the moon, as their weights to its weight. Add, that since Jupiter's satellites revolve in times that are in a sesquiplicate ratio of their distances from the centre of Jupiter, and consequently at equal distances from Jupiter, their accelerating gravities are equal; therefore, falling equal altitudes in equal times, they will describe equal spaces; just as heavy bodies do on our earth. And the same argument will hold of the primary planets with regard to the sun. And the powers whereby unequal bodies are equally accelerated, are as the bodies; *i.e.* the weigths are as the quantities of matter in the planets. And the weights of the primary and secundary planets towards the sun, are as the quantities of matter in the planets and satellites. And hence are several corollaries drawn, relating to the weights of bodies on the surface of the earth, magnetism, and the existence of a vacuum. Which see under the articles VACUUM, WEIGHT, and MAGNETISM.

5°. Gravity extents itself towards all bodies, and is in proportion to the quantity of matter in each.

That all the planets gravitate towards each other, has been already shewn; likewise, that the gravity towards any one considered apart, is reciprocally as the square of its distance from the centre of the planet: Consequently, gravity is proportional to the matter therein. Farther, as all the parts of any planet, A, gravitate towards another planet, B; and the gravity of any part is to the gravity of the whole, as the matter of the part to the matter of the whole; and reaction equal to action: The planet B will gravitate towards all the parts of the planet A; and its gravity towards any part, will be to its gravity towards the whole, as the matter of the part to the matter of the whole.

Hence, we derive methods of finding and comparing the gravities of bodies towards different planets; of finding the quantities of matter in the several planets, and their densities; since the weights of equal bodies revolving about planets, are as the diameters of their orbits directly, and as the squares of the periodical times, inversly; and the weights at any distance from the centre of the planet are greater or less in a duplicate ratio of their distances, inversly: And since the quantities of matter in the planets are as the powers at equal distances from their centres: And, lastly, since the weights of equal and homogeneous bodies towards homogeneous spheres, are, at the surfaces of the spheres, as the diameters of those spheres; and, consequently the densities of the heterogeneous bodies are as the weights at the distances of the diameters of the spheres. See DENSITY.

6°. The common centre of gravity of the sun, and all the planets, is at rest: And the sun, though always in motion, yet never recedes far from the common centre of all the planets.

For, the matter in the sun being to that in Jupiter as 1033 to 1; and Jupiter's distance from the sun to the semidiameter of the sun in a ratio somewhat bigger; the common centre of gravity of Jupiter and the sun will be found a point a little without the sun's surface. And, by the same means, the common centre of Saturn and the sun, will be found a point a little within the sun's surface. And the common centre of the earth, and all the planets, will be scarce one diameter of the sun distant from the centre thereof. But the centre is always at rest:

Therefore, though the sun will have a motion this and that way, according to the various situations of the planets, yet it can never recede far from the centre. So that the common centre of gravity of the earth, sun, and planets, may be esteemed the centre of the whole world. See SUN and CENTER.

7°. The planets move in ellipses that have their foci in the center of the sun; and describe areas proportional to their times.

This we have already laid down à posteriori, as a phænomenon: And now, that the principle of the heavenly motions is shewn, we deduce it therefrom à priori. Thus: Since the weights of the planets towards the sun are reciprocally as the squares of their distances from the centre of the sun; if the sun were at rest, and the other planets did not act on each other; their oribits would be elliptical, having the sun in their common umbilicus; and would describe areas proportional to the times: But the mutual actions of the planets are very small, and may be well thrown aside. Therefore, &c. See PLANET and ORBIT.

Indeed, the action of Jupiter on Saturn is of some consequence; and hence, according to the different situations and distances of those two planets, their orbits will be a little disturbed.

The sun's orbit too, is sensibly disturbed by the action of the moon: And the common centre of the two describes an ellipsis round the sun placed in the umbilicus; and with a radius drawn to the centre of the sun, describes areas proportional to the times. See EARTH and SATURN.

8°. The aphelia and nodes of the planets are at rest. Excepting for some inconsiderable irregularities arising from the actions of the revolving planets and comets.—Consequently, as the fixed stars retain their position to the aphelia and nodes; they, too, are at rest. See NODE, STAR, &c.

9°. The axis, or polar diameter of the planets, is less than the equatorial diameter.

The planets, had they no diurnal rotation, would be spheres; as having an equal gravity on every side: But by this rotation, the parts receding from the axis endeavour to rise towards the equator, which, if the matter they consist of be fluid, will be effected very sensibly. Accordingly Jupiter, whose density is found not much to exceed that of water on our globe, is observed by the astronomers to be considerably less between the poles, than from east to west. And, on the same principle, unless our earth were higher at the equator than towards the poles, the sea would rise under the equator, and overflow all near it. See SPHEROID.

But this figure of the earth Sir Isaac Newton proves likewise à posteriori; from the oscillations of pendulums being slower, and smaller, in the equatorial, than the polar parts of the globe. See PENDULUM.

10°. All the moon's motions, and all the inequalities in those motions, follow from these principles: e.gr. Her unequal velocity, and that of her nodes, and apogee in the syzyges and quadratures; the differences in her eccentricity, and her variation, &c. See MOON, QUADRATURE, SYZYGY, &c.

11°. From the inequalities in the lunar motions, we can deduce the several inequalities in the motions of the satellites. See SATELLITES.

12°. From these principles, particularly the action of the sun and moon upon the earth, it follows, that we must have tides; or that the sea must swell and subside twice every day. See TIDES.

13°. Hence likewise follows, the whole theory of comets; as, that they are above the region of the moon, and in the planetary spaces; that they shine by the sun's light reflected from them; that they move in conic sections, whose umbilici are in the centre of the sun; and by radii drawn to the sun, describe areas proportional to the times; that their orbits, or trajectories, are very nearly parabolas; that their bodies are solid, compact, &c. like those of the planets, and must therefore acquire an immense heat in their perihelia; that their tails are exhalations arising from them, and encompassing them like atmospheres. See COMET.

The objections raised against this philosophy, are chiefly aimed at the principle gravity; which some condemn as an *occult quality*, and others as a *miraculous* and preter-natural cause; neither of which have longer any room in sound philosophy. Others, again, set it aside, as destroying the notion of vortices; and others, as supposing a vacuum. But these are all abundantly obviated under the articles GRAVITY, ATTRACTION, VORTEX; VACUUM, QUALITY, &c.

Chapter 11: Science in the Scottish Enlightenment

11.1 Extract from: J. Hutton, *Abstract of a dissertation read in the Royal Society of Edinburgh . . . concerning the system of the earth, its duration and stability.* Reprinted (intro. J. Craig) as *The 1785 Abstract.* Edinburgh: Scottish Academic Press, 1987

The purpose of this Dissertation is to form some estimate with regard to the time the globe of this Earth has existed, as a world maintaining plants and animals; to reason with regard to the changes which the earth has undergone; and to see how far an end or termination to this system of things may be perceived, from the consideration of that which has already come to pass.

As it is not in human record, but in natural history, that we are to look for the means of ascertaining what has already been, it is here proposed to examine the appearances of the earth, in order to be informed of operations which have been transacted in time past. It is thus that, from principles of natural philosophy, we may arrive at some knowledge of order and system in the economy of this globe, and may form a rational opinion with regard to the course of nature, or to events which are in time to happen.

The solid parts of the present land appear, in general, to have been composed of the productions of the sea, and of other materials similar to those now found upon the shores. Hence we find reason to conclude,

1st, That the land on which we rest is not simple and original, but that it is a composition, and had been formed by the operation of second causes.

2dly, That, before the present land was made, there had subsisted a world composed of sea and land, in which were tides and currents, with such operations at the bottom of the sea as now take place. And,

Lastly, That, while the present land was forming at the bottom of the ocean, the former land maintained plants and animals; at least, the sea was then inhabited by animals, in a similar manner as it is at present.

Hence we are led to conclude, that the greater part of our land, if not the whole, had been produced by operations natural to this globe; but that, in order to make this land a permanent body, resisting the operations of the waters, two things had been required; 1st, The consolidation of masses formed by collections of loose or incoherent materials; 2dly, The elevation of those consolidated masses from the bottom of the sea, the place where they were collected, to the stations in which they now remain above the level of the ocean. [. . .]

Thus the subject is considered as naturally divided into two branches, to be separately examined: *First,* by what natural operation strata of loose materials had been formed into solid masses; *Secondly,* By what power of nature the consolidated strata at the bottom of the sea had been transformed into land.

With regard to the *first* of these, the consolidation of strata, there are two ways in which this operation may be conceived to have been performed; first, by means of the solution of bodies in water, and the after concretion of these dissolved substances, when separated from their solvent; *secondly,* the fusion of bodies by means of heat, and the subsequent congelation of those consolidating substances. [. . .]

With regard to the other probable means, heat and fusion, these are found to be perfectly competent for producing the end in view, as every kind of substance may by heat be rendered soft, or brought into fusion, and as strata are actually found consolidated with every different species of substance. [. . .]

Having come to this general conclusion, that heat and fusion, not aqueous solution, had preceded the consolidation of the loose materials collected at the bottom of the sea, those consolidated strata, in general, are next examined, in order to discover other appearances, by which the doctrine may be either confirmed or refuted. Here the changes of strata, from their natural state of continuity, by veins and fissures, are considered; and the clearest evidence is hence deduced, that the strata have been consolidated by means of fusion, and not by aqueous solution; for, not only are strata in general found intersected with veins and cutters, an appearance inconsistent with their having been consolidated simply by previous solution; but, in proportion as strata are more or less consolidated, they are found with the proper corresponding appearances of veins and fissures.

With regard to the second branch, in considering by what power the consolidated strata had been transformed into land, or raised above the level of the sea, it is supposed that the same power of extreme heat, by which every different mineral substance had been brought into a melted state, might be capable of producing an expansive force, sufficient for elevating the land, from the bottom of the ocean, to the place it now occupies above the surface of the sea. Here we are again referred to nature, in examining how far the strata, formed by successive sediments or accumulations deposited at the bottom of the sea, are to be found in that regular state, which would necessarily take place in their original production; or if, on the other hand, they are actually changed in their natural situation, broken, twisted, and confounded, as might be expected, from the operation of subterranean heat, and violent expansion. But, as strata are actually found in every degree of fracture, flexure, and contortion, consistent with this supposition, and with no other, we are led to conclude, that our land had been raised above the surface of the sea, in order to become a habitable world; as well as that it had been consolidated by means of the same power of subterranean heat, in order to remain above the level of the sea, and to resist the violent efforts of the ocean.

This theory is next confirmed by the examination of mineral veins, those great fissures of the earth, which contain matter perfectly foreign to the strata they traverse; matter evidently derived from the mineral region, that is, from the place where the active power of fire, and the expansive force of heat, reside.

Such being considered as the operations of the mineral region, we are hence directed to look for the manifestation of this power and force, in the appearances of nature. It is here we find eruptions of ignited matter from the scattered volcano's of the globe; and these we conclude to be the effects of such a power precisely as that above which we now inquire. Volcano's are thus considered as the proper discharges of a superfluous or redundant power; not as things accidental in the course of nature, but as useful for the safety of mankind, and as forming a natural ingredient in the constitution of the globe.

Lastly, The extension of this theory, respecting mineral strata, to all parts of the globe, is made, by finding a perfect similarity in the solid land through all the earth, although, in particular places, it is attended with peculiar productions, with which the present inquiry is not concerned.

A theory is thus formed, with regard to a mineral system. In this system, hard and solid bodies are to be formed from soft bodies, from loose or incoherent materials, collected together at the bottom of the sea; and the bottom of the ocean is to be made to change its place with relation to the centre of the earth, to be formed into land above the level of the sea, and to become a country fertile and inhabited.

That there is nothing visionary in this theory, appears from its having been rationally deduced from natural events, from things which have already happened; things which have left, in the particular constitutions of bodies, proper traces of the manner of their production; and things which may be examined with all the accuracy, or reasoned upon with all the light, that science can afford. As it is only by employing science in this manner, that philosophy enlightens man with the knowledge of that wisdom or design which is to be found in nature, the system now proposed, from unquestionable principles, will claim the attention of scientific men, and may be admitted in our speculations with regard to the works of nature, notwithstanding many steps in the progress may remain unknown.

By thus proceeding upon investigated principles, we are led to conclude, that, if this part of the earth which we now inhabit had been produced, in the course of time, from the materials of a former earth, we should, in the examination of our land, find data from which to reason, with regard to the nature of that world, which had existed during the period of time in which the present earth was forming; and thus we might be brought to understand the nature of that earth which had preceded this; how far it had been similar to the present, in producing plants and nourishing animals. But this interesting point is perfectly ascertained, by finding abundance of every manner of vegetable production, as well as the several species of marine bodies, in the strata of our earth.

Having thus ascertained a regular system, in which the present land of the globe had been first formed at the bottom of the ocean, and then raised above the surface of the sea, a question naturally occurs with regard to time; what had been the space of time necessary for accomplishing this great work?

In order to form a judgement concerning this subject, our attention is directed to another progress in the system of the globe, namely, the destruction of the land which had preceded that on which we dwell. [. . .]

If we could measure the progress of the present land, towards its dissolution by attrition, and its submersion in the ocean, we might discover the actual duration of a former earth; an earth which had supported plants and animals, and had supplied the ocean with those materials which the construction of the present earth required; consequently, we should have the measure of a corresponding space of time, viz. that which had been required in the production of the present land. [. . .]

But, as there is not in human observation proper means for measuring the waste of land upon the globe, it is hence inferred, that we cannot estimate the duration of what we see at present, nor calculate the period at which it had begun; so that, with respect to human observation, this world has neither a beginning nor an end.

An endeavour is then made to support the theory by an argument of a moral nature, drawn from the consideration of a final cause. Here a comparison is formed between the present theory, and those by which there is necessarily implied either evil or disorder in natural things; and an argument is formed, upon the supposed wisdom of nature, for the justness of a theory in which perfect order is to be perceived. For,

According to the theory, a soil, adapted to the growth of plants, is necessarily prepared, and carefully preserved; and, in the necessary waste of land which is inhabited, the foundation is laid for future continents, in order to support the system of this living world.

Thus, either in supposing Nature wise and good, an argument is formed in confirmation of the theory, or, in supposing the theory to be just, an argument may be established for wisdom and benevolence to be perceived in nature. In this manner, there is opened to our view a subject interesting to man who thinks; a subject on which to reason with relation to the system of nature; and one which may afford the human mind both information and entertainment.

11.2 Joseph Black, 'Experiments upon Magnesia Alba, Quicklime and some other Alkaline Substances', *Essays and Observations, Physical and Literary*, Edinburgh, 1756, pp. 157–225. Alembic Club Reprint, 1944, No. 1, pp. 10–20, *passim*

MAGNESIA is quickly dissolved with violent effervescence, or explosion of air, by the acids of vitriol, nitre, and of common salt, and by distilled vinegar; the neutral saline liquors thence produced having each their peculiar properties.

THAT which is made with the vitriolic acid, may be condensed into crystals similar in all respects to epsom-salt.

THAT which is made with the nitrous is of a yellow colour, and yields saline crystals, which retain their form in a very dry air, but melt in a moist one.

THAT which is produced by means of spirit of salt, yields no crystals; and if evaporated to dryness, soon melts again when exposed to the air.

THAT which is obtained from the union of distilled vinegar with *magnesia*, affords no crystals by evaporation, but is condensed into a saline mass, which, while warm, is extremely tough and viscid, very much resembling a strong glue both in colour and consistence, and becomes brittle when cold.

By these experiments *magnesia* appears to be a substance very different from those of the calcarious class; under which I would be understood to comprehend all those that are converted into a perfect quick-lime in a strong fire, such as *lime-stone, marble, chalk*, those *spars* and *marles* which effervesce with aqua fortis, all *animal shells* and the bodies called *lithophyta*. All of these, by being joined with acids, yield a set of compounds which are very different from those we have just now described. Thus, if a small quantity of any calcarious matter be reduced to a fine powder and thrown into spirit of vitriol, it is attacked by this acid with a brisk effervescence; but little or no dissolution ensues. It absorbs the acid, and remains united with it in the form of a white powder, at the bottom of the vessel; while the liquor has hardly any taste, and shews only a very light cloud upon the addition of alkali.*

THE same white powder is also formed when spirit of vitriol is added to a calcarious earth dissolved in any other acid; the vitriolic expelling the other acid, and joining itself to the earth by a stronger attraction; [. . .]

THREE drams of *magnesia* in fine powder, an ounce of salt ammoniac, and six ounces of water were mixed together, and digested six days in a retort joined to a receiver.

DURING the whole time, the neck of the retort was pointed a little upwards, and the most watery part of the vapour, which was condensed there, fell back into its body. In the beginning of the experiment, a volatile salt was therefore collected in a dry form in the receiver, and afterwards dissolved into spirit.

WHEN all was cool, I found in the retort a saline liquor, some undissolved *magnesia*, and some salt ammoniac crystallized. The saline liquor was separated from the other two, and then mixed with the alkaline spirit. A coagulum was immediately formed, and a *magnesia* precipitated from the mixture.

---

* Mr. *Margraaf* has lately demonstrated, by a set of curious and accurate experiments, that this powder is of the nature, and possesses the properties, of the gypseous or selenitic substances. That such substances can be resolved into vitriolic acid and calcarious earth, and can be again composed by joining these two ingredients together. Mem. de l'Acad. de Berlin. an. 1750, p. 144.

THE *magnesia* which had remained in the retort, when well washed and dried, weighed two scruples and fifteen grains.

WE learn by the latter part of this experiment, that the attraction of the volatile alkali for acids is stronger than that of *magnesia*, since it separated this powder from the acid to which it was joined. But it also appears, that a gentle heat is capable of overcoming this superiority of attraction, and of gradually elevating the alkali, while it leaves the less volatile acid with the *magnesia*.

DISSOLVE a dram of any calcarious substance in the acid of nitre or of common salt, taking care that the solution be rendered perfectly neutral, or that no superfluous acid be added. Mix with this solution a dram of *magnesia* in fine powder, and digest it in the heat of boiling water about twenty four hours; then dilute the mixture with double its quantity of water, and filtrate. The greatest part of the earth now left in the filtre is calcarious, and the liquor which passed thro', if mixed with a dissolved alkali; yields a white powder, the largest portion of which is a true *magnesia*.

FROM this experiment it appears, that an acid quits a calcarious earth to join itself to *magnesia*; but the exchange being performed slowly, some of the *magnesia* is still undissolved, and part of the calcarious earth remains yet joined to the acid. [. . .]

QUICK-LIME itself is also rendered mild by *magnesia*, if these two are well rubbed together and infused with a small quantity of water.

BY the following experiments, I proposed to know whether this substance could be reduced to a quick-lime.

AN ounce of *magnesia* was exposed in a crucible for about an hour to such a heat as is sufficient to melt copper. When taken out, it weighed three drams and one scruple, or had lost $\frac{7}{12}$ of its former weight.

I repeated, with the *magnesia* prepared in this manner, most of those experiments I had already made upon it before calcination, and the result was as follows.

IT dissolves in all the acids, and with these composes salts exactly similar to those described in the first set of experiments; but what is particularly to be remarked, it is dissolved without any the least degree of effervescence.

IT slowly precipitates the corrosive sublimate of mercury in the form of a black powder.

IT separates the volatile alkali in salt ammoniac from the acid, when it is mixed with a warm solution of that salt. But it does not separate an acid from a calcarious earth, nor does it induce the least change upon lime-water.

LASTLY, when a dram of it is digested with an ounce of water in a bottle for some hours, it does not make any the least change in the water. The *magnesia*, when dried, is found to have gained ten grains; but it neither effervesces with acids, nor does it sensibly affect lime-water.

OBSERVING *magnesia* to lose such a remarkable proportion of its weight in the fire, my next attempts were directed to the investigation of this volatile part, and, among other experiments, the following seemed to throw some light upon it.

THREE ounces of *magnesia* were distilled in a glass retort and receiver, the fire being gradually increased until the *magnesia* was obscurely red hot. When all was cool, I found only five drams of a whitish water in the receiver, which had a faint smell of the spirit of hartshorn, gave a green colour to the juice of violets, and rendered the solutions of corrosive sublimate and of silver very slightly turbid. But it did not sensibly effervesce with acids.

THE *magnesia* when taken out of the retort, weighed an ounce, three drams, and thirty grains, or had lost more than the half of its weight. It still effervesced pretty briskly with acids, tho' not so strongly as before this operation.

THE fire should have been raised here to the degree requisite for the perfect calcination of *magnesia*. But even from this imperfect experiment, it is evident, that of the volatile parts contained in that powder, a small proportion only is water; the rest cannot, it seems, be retained in vessels, under a visible form. Chemists have often observed, in their distillations, that part of a body has vanished from their senses, notwithstanding the utmost care to retain it; and they have always found, upon further inquiry, that subtile part to be air, which having been imprisoned in the body, under a solid form was set free and rendered fluid and elastic by the fire. We may therefore safely conclude, that the volatile matter, lost in the calcination of *magnesia*, is mostly air; and hence the calcined *magnesia* does not emit air, or make an effervescence, when mixed with acids.

THE water, from its properties, seems to contain a small portion of volatile alkali, which was probably formed from the earth, air, and water, or from some of these combined together; and perhaps also from a small quantity of inflammable matter which adhered accidentally to the *magnesia*. Whenever Chemists meet with this salt, they are inclined to ascribe its origin to some animal, or putrid vegetable, substance; and this they have always done, when they obtained it from the calcarious earths, all of which afford a small quantity of it. There is, however, no doubt that it can sometimes be produced independently of any such mixture, since many fresh vegetables and tartar afford a considerable quantity of it. And how can it, in the present instance, be supposed, that any animal or vegetable matter adhered to the *magnesia*, while it was dissolved by an acid, separated from this by an alkali, and washed with so much water?

TWO drams of *magnesia* were calcined in a crucible, in the manner described above, and thus reduced to two scruples and twelve grains. This calcined *magnesia* was dissolved in a sufficient quantity of spirit of vitriol, and then again separated from the acid by the addition of an alkali, of which a large quantity is necessary for this purpose. The *magnesia* being very well washed and dryed, weighed one dram and fifty grains. It effervesced violently, or emitted a large quantity of air, when thrown into acids, formed a red powder when mixed with a solution of sublimate, separated the calcarious earths from an acid, and sweetened lime-water: and had thus recovered all those properties which it had but just now lost by calcination: nor had it only recovered its original properties, but acquired besides an addition of weight nearly equal to what had been lost in the fire; and, as it is found to effervesce with acids, part of the addition must certainly be air.

THIS air seems to have been furnished by the alkali from which it was separated by the acid; for Dr. *Hales* has clearly proved, that alkaline salts contain a large quantity of fixed air, which they emit in great abundance when joined to a pure acid. In the present case, the alkali is really joined to an acid, but without any visible emission of air; and yet the air is not retained in it: for the neutral salt, into which it is converted, is the same in quantity, and in every other respect, as if the acid employed had not been previously saturated with *magnesia*, but offered to the alkali in its pure state, and had driven the air out of it in their conflict. It seems therefore evident, that the air was forced from the alkali by the acid, and lodged itself in the *magnesia*.

THESE considerations led me to try a few experiments, whereby I might know what quantity of air is expelled from an alkali, or from *magnesia*, by acids.

TWO drams of a pure fixed alkaline salt, and an ounce of water, were put into a Florentine flask, which, together with its contents, weighed two ounces and two drams. Some oil of vitriol diluted with water was dropt in, until the salt was exactly saturated; which it was found to be, when two drams, two scruples, and three grains of this acid had been added. The vial with its contents now weighed two ounces, four drams, and fifteen grains. One scruple, therefore, and eight grains were lost during the ebullition, of which a trifling portion may be water, or something of the same kind. The rest is air.

Some oil of vitriol diluted with water was dropt in, until the salt was exactly saturated; which it was found to be, when two drams, two scruples, and three grains of this acid had been added. The vial with its contents now weighed two ounces, four drams, and fifteen grains. One scruple, therefore, and eight grains were lost during the ebullition, of which a trifling portion may be water, or something of the same kind. The rest is air. [. . .]

THE celebrated *Homberg* has attempted to estimate the quantity of solid salt contained in a determined portion of the several acids. He saturated equal quantities of an alkali with each of them; and, observing the weight which the alkali had gained, after being perfectly dried, took this for the quantity of solid salt contained in that share of the acid which performed the saturation. But we learn from the above experiment, that his estimate was not accurate, because the alkali loses weight as well as gains it.

TWO drams of *magnesia*, treated exactly as the alkali in the last experiment, were just dissolved by four drams, one scruple, and seven grains of the same acid liquor, and lost one scruple and sixteen grains by the ebullition.

Two drams of *magnesia* were reduced, by the action of a violent fire, to two scruples and twelve grains, with which the same process was repeated, as in the two last experiments; four drams, one scruple, and two grains of the same acid were required to compleat the solution, and no weight was lost in the experiment.

As in the separation of the volatile from the fixed parts of bodies, by means of heat, a small quantity of the latter is generally raised with the former; so the air and water, originally contained in the *magnesia*, and afterwards dissipated by the fire, seem to have carried off a small part of the fixed earth of this substance. This is probably the reason, why calcined *magnesia* is saturated with a quantity of acid, somewhat less than what is required to dissolve it before calcination; and the same may be assigned as one cause which hinders us from restoring the whole of its original weight, by solution and precipitation.

I took care to dilute the vitriolic acid, in order to avoid the heat and ebullition which it would otherwise have excited in the water; and I chose a Florentine flask, on account of its lightness, capacity, and shape, which is peculiarly adapted to the experiment; for the vapours raised by the ebullition circulated for a short time, thro' the wide cavity of the vial, but were soon collected upon its sides, like dew, and none of them seemed to reach the neck, which continued perfectly dry to the end of the experiment.

We now perceive the reason, why crude and calcined *magnesia*, which differ in many respects from one another, agree however in composing the same kind of salt, when dissolved in any particular acid; for the crude *magnesia* seems to differ from the calcined chiefly by containing a considerable quantity of air, which air is unavoidably dissipated and lost during the dissolution.

From our experiments, it seems probable, that the increase of weight which some metals acquire, by being first dissolved in acids, and then separated from them again by alkalis, proceeds from air furnished by the alkalis. [. . .]

The above experiments lead us also to conclude, that volatile alkalis, and the common absorbent earths, which lose their air by being joined to acids, but shew evident signs of their having recovered it, when separated from them by alkalis, received it from these alkalis which lost it in the instant of their joining with the acid.

11.3 Adam Smith, *Essays on Philosophical Subjects*, ed. W. P. D. Wightman and J. C. Bryce, 1980. Oxford: Clarendon Press

When one accustomed object appears after another, which it does not usually follow, it first excites, by its unexpectedness, the sentiment properly called Surprise, and afterwards, by the singularity of the succession, or order of its appearance, the sentiment properly called Wonder. We start and are surprised at feeling it there, and then wonder how it came there. The motion of a small piece of iron along a plain table is in itself no extraordinary object, yet the person who first saw it begin, without any visible impulse, in consequence of the motion of a loadstone at some little distance from it could not behold it without the most extreme Surprise; and when that momentary emotion was over, he would still wonder how it came to be conjoined to an event with which, according to the ordinary train of things, he could have so little suspected it to have any connection.

When two objects, however unlike, have often been observed to follow each other, and have constantly presented themselves to the senses in that order, they come to be so connected together in the fancy, that the idea of the one seems, of its own accord, to call up and introduce that of the other. If the objects are still observed to succeed each other as before, this connection, or, as it has been called, this association of their ideas, becomes stricter and stricter, and the habit of the imagination to pass from the conception of the one to that of the other, grows more and more rivetted and confirmed. As its ideas move more rapidly than external objects, it is continually running before them, and therefore anticipates, before it happens, every event which falls out according to this ordinary course of things. When objects succeed each other in the same train in which the ideas of the imagination have thus been accustomed to move, and in which, though not conducted by that chain of events presented to the senses, they have acquired a tendency to go on of their own accord, such objects appear all closely connected with one another, and the thought glides easily along them, without effort and without interruption. They fall in with the natural career of the imagination; and as the ideas which represented such a train of things would seem all mutually to introduce each other, every last thought to be called up by the foregoing, and to call up the succeeding; so when the objects themselves occur, every last event seems, in the same manner, to be introduced by the foregoing, and to introduce the succeeding. There is no break, no stop, no gap, no interval. The ideas excited by so coherent a chain of things seem, as it were, to float through the mind of their own accord, without obliging it to exert itself, or to make any effort in order to pass from one to them to another.

But if this customary connection be interrupted, if one or more objects appear in an order quite different from that to which the imagination has been accustomed, and for which it is prepared, the contrary of all this happens. We are at first surprised by the unexpectedness of the new appearance, and when that momentary emotion is over, we still wonder how it came to occur in that place. The imagination no longer feels the usual facility of passing from the event which goes before to that which comes after. It is an order or law of succession to which it has not been accustomed, and which it therefore finds some difficulty in following, or in attending to. The fancy is stopped and interrupted in that natural movement or career, according to which it was proceeding. Those two events seem to stand at a distance from each other; it endeavours to bring them together, but they refuse to unite; and it feels, or imagines it feels, something like a gap or interval betwixt them. It naturally hesitates, and, as it were, pauses upon the brink of this interval; it endeavours to find out something which may fill up the gap, which, like a bridge, may so far at least unite those seemingly distant objects, as to render the passage of the thought betwixt them smooth, and natural, and easy. The supposition of a chain of intermediate, though invisible, events, which succeed each other in a train similar to that in which the imagination has been accustomed to move, and which link together those two disjointed appearances, is the only means by which the imagination can fill up this interval, is the only bridge which, if one may say so, can smooth its passage from the one object to the other. Thus, when we observe the motion of the iron, in consequence of that of the loadstone, we gaze and hesitate, and feel a want of connection betwixt two events which follow one another in so unusual a train. But when, with Des Cartes, we imagine certain invisible effluvia to circulate round one of them, and by their repeated impulses to impel the other, both to move towards it, and to follow its motion, we fill up the interval betwixt them, we join them together by a sort of bridge, and thus take off that hesitation and difficulty which the imagination felt in passing from the one to the other. That the iron should move after the loadstone seems, upon this hypothesis, in some measure according to the ordinary course of things. Motion after impulse is an order of succession with which of all things we are the most familiar. Two objects which are so connected seem no longer to be disjoined, and the imagination flows smoothly and easily along them. [. . .]

Philosophy is the science of the connecting principles of nature. Nature, after the largest experience that common observation can acquire, seems to abound with events which appear solitary and incoherent with all that go before them, which therefore disturb the easy movement of the imagination; which make its ideas succeed each other, if one may say so, by irregular starts and sallies; and which thus tend, in some measure, to introduce those confusions and distractions we formerly mentioned. Philosophy, by representing the invisible chains which bind together all these disjointed objects, endeavours to introduce order into this chaos of jarring and discordant appearances, to allay this tumult of the imagination, and to restore it, when it surveys the great revolutions of the universe, to that tone of tranquillity and composure, which is both most agreeable in itself, and most suitable to its nature.

Chapter 12: Science on the fringe of Europe: Eighteenth-century Sweden

12.1 A Celsius, 'A barometrical experiment', *Phil. Trans.*, 1724, 33, p. 89 [Abridged edition]

For observing the variation of the column of mercury in the barometer, according to different heights in the atmosphere, the deep mines in Sweden may be reckoned peculiarly adapted. For not only their depth may be measured with great accuracy, but also the whole observation performed in a short time: an advantage often wanting in making the like experiments on high mountains. If therefore a great many experiments were made in different mines, no doubt but the true progression, by which the density of the air decreases, would at length be discovered.

Aug. 28, 1724, M. Celsius made the following experiment in the Salan silver mine, about 7 miles to the west of Upsal. At the entry to the queen Christina's shaft, he observed the height of the mercury at 30.38 inches, or the $\frac{8098}{1800}$ of a Swedish foot; he was then let down with the barometer in a vessel by a rope, to the depth of 636 feet, where he observed the mercury ascend to 30.98 inches: from thence being drawn up again to the mouth of the shaft, he observed the column of mercury at the same height as before, viz. 30.38 inches. So that the mercury raised to the height of 636 feet in the air, falls 6 lines or $\frac{6}{180}$ parts of a foot; and consequently, if the air were supposed of equal density every where, the variation of one line in the column of mercury would answer to 106 feet perpendicular height. During the time of the observation, there was a little rain and wind; yet no sensible alteration could be observed at the same time in the column of mercury in another barometer, fixed to a wall above the mine.

Next day, the sky being serene and calm, the mercury stood at 30.36 inches at the foot of the church of Sale, not far from the mine; but going up 145 feet high in the tower of the said church, he found the mercury at 30.23 inches: so that the height of 111 feet and $\frac{7}{8}$ parts answers to the descent of one line in the barometer.

That this observation may be duly compared with the experiments of this kind, made by others, it is to be noted, that the ratio between the Swedish and Paris foot royal is nearly that of 1000 to 1096, or 125 to 137, as Mr. Celsius accurately observed by comparing them together.

12.2 Lecture Advertisement for M. Triewald, 1725: National Library of Scotland [Facsimile]

WHereas JOHN THOROLD and MARTIN TRIEWALD, at the Defire and Invitation of fome Gentlemen of this City [*To come from England to Perform a* COURSE *of NATURAL and EXPERIMENTAL* PHILOSOPHY *at Edinburgh*] came hither, and iffued out their *Propofals*, fetting forth, " That their COURSE was to commence in *December* " laft, confifting of 28 *LECTURES*, to be read three Times a-week, namely, " on *Monday*, *Wednefday* and *Friday*, and to begin at Five a-clock in the Even- " ing; That the *Rate* of the COURSE was to be Two Guineas to each Gentle- " man; and that, for their Satisfaction and Encouragement, they annexed to " their forefaid *Propofals*, a Lift of all the *Inftruments* us'd in the *Experiments*; " as well as an Account of the Order of the COURSE of *Mechanical*, *Optical*, " *Hydroftatical* and *Pneumatical Experiments*, to be made during the 28 *LEC-* " *TURES*". And altho' the PROPOSERS defign'd now to return to *England*, having finifhed their forefaid COURSE, to the entire Satisfaction of thofe who attended it; Yet fince a great many other Gentlemen are now earneftly defirous of *Subfcribing* to a Second COURSE at the forefaid *Rate*, to begin upon *Monday* the Twelfth Day of *April* next, at Five of the Clock that Afternoon, at *Skinner's-ball*; where the numerous and coftly *Apparatus* are fitted up, and the Air Gun, and many other new *Inftruments* to be us'd in this Second COURSE, are to be got ready by that Day: THEREFORE, in Compliance with this their Defire, they are refolved once more to Perform a new COURSE, commencing Time and Place forefaid, and that on fuch and fo many Days and Hours of the Week, as fhall then be fettled by Majority of the *Subfcribers*; this Second COURSE being to contain not only all the *Experiments* of the Former, but alfo many confiderable Ones which are entirely new; the proper *Inftruments* for that End having been but lately purchaf'd. The whole COURSE will be found to be very Ufeful and Inftructive, not only to thofe who have ftudied the *Mathematicks*, but even to fuch as are not at all acquainted with that Science; and thereby the Latter, as well as the Former, will, with a great Deal of Eafe and Pleafure, come to the Knowledge of thofe Things, fo abfolutely requifite to be known by all Perfons of any Profeffion or Employment whatfoever; which otherwife cannot be attained without the greateft Labour, Application and Lofs of Time, as well as a vaft Expence in purchafing the proper *Inftruments*. Such Gentlemen who intend to take the Benefit of this Second COURSE, (which is to be the laft in this City) are therefore defir'd, before, or on the Tenth Day of *April* next, to give in their Names to the PROPOSERS, at Mr. *Jones's* at the Foot of *Skinner's Clofs*; for unlefs fuch a fuitable Number of Gentlemens Names be given in before, or on the faid Tenth Day of *April* next, fo as the PROPOSERS may meet with a proper Encouragement for their Pains and great Charges in carrying on their COURSE, they defign to depart the City.

E D I N B U R G H:

Printed for Mr. *WILLIAM ROLLAND*, by Mr. *THOMAS RUDDIMAN*, at his Printing-houfe in *Moroco's* Clofe, the 4th Storey of the Turnpike near the Foot thereof, oppofite to the Head of *Libertoun's* Wynd, in the *Lawn-market*. 1725. Where Advertifements and Subfcriptions are taken in.

Advertifements and *Subfcriptions* are likewife taken in at the Shop of Mr *ALEXANDER STMMER* in the Parliament Clofs; where the *Mercury* is alfo fold,

(*Price Three Halfpence.*)

12.3 P. Wargentin, 'On the variation of the magnetic needle', *Phil. Trans.*, 1752, 47, pp. 165–6 [Abridged edition]

Dr. Halley suspected that there was some correspondence between the aurora borealis and the magnetic needle. And Celsius and Hiorter found by experiments that the needle was greatly disturbed, and unsteady, whenever the northern lights rose to the zenith or passed southward, so as that the declination seemed to follow the motion of the light, and in a very few minutes of time would sometimes vary 3 or 4 degrees. M. Wargentin has also, by observations in Feb. 1750, like as Graham, Celsius, and others, observed before, found that there is a diurnal variation of the needle backward and forward: so as that from 7 in the morning till 2 afternoon, the needle declined more and more to the west by $\frac{1}{3}$ or $\frac{1}{4}$ part of a degree; after which it gradually returned again, so as by 8 at night to be nearly the same as it was at 8 in the morning. After this it is nearly at rest during the rest of the night, except some small motion to the west about midnight. And this diurnal variation never fails, but is constant and almost regular, unless when it is impeded by the northern lights. This he observed constantly from the 1st of February to the 15th, on which last day an aurora borealis appeared, and deranged the needle so, as in 10 minutes time, about 10 at night, it shifted 20' to the west, and in another ten minutes returned thirty-seven minutes to the east. But on the lights disappearing, the needle settled at rest. And thus it continued in its regular diurnal vibrations, till Feb. 28, when it was again disturbed by another appearance of the northern lights, so as to cause the needle to vibrate irregularly between 6° 50' and 9° 1' of west variation. And on the 2d of April, from a like cause, it differed from itself little less than 5°, shifting irregularly and frequently backward and forward, between 4° 56' and 9° 55'.

12.4 C. Linnaeus, Dedication and Preface to *Species Plantarum*, 1753; trans. W. T. Stearn, 1957, pp. 152–5. London: Ray Society

MOST MIGHTY ALL GRACIOUS

KING AND QUEEN

ADOLPH FRIDERIC,

LOVISA ULRICA,

OF THE SWEDES GOTHS AND WENDS

KING AND QUEEN!

TO YOUR MAJESTIES I most humbly owe this work, the fruit of the greatest and best part of my life, which under YOUR MAJESTIES' genial reign I now complete with a contented and tranquil mind.

YOUR MAJESTIES, from your first happy arrival in this kingdom, have looked upon me with kindly eyes, called me to Your Court and expressed towards me all Royal grace.

YOUR MAJESTIES have also given the Sciences which I follow light and prestige in Your Realm, since YOUR MAJESTIES have not only most graciously had the Creator's wondrous work described for you but have also assembled representative products of all three realms of Nature and have commanded them to be installed within your splendid palaces at Ulriksdahl and Drottningholm where, as representatives of the whole wide world, they can daily come before the eyes of YOUR MAJESTIES.

Believe me that I do not say too much when I openly admit that from the time of the wise King Solomon and the Queen of rich Arabia no Sovereigns have shown greater respect for the wonders of the Almighty Creator.

For this Science ought and shall vie with all other monuments to make YOUR MAJESTIES' names undying, by imprinting them in Nature's own book, which every year is issued anew, being as lasting as the Terrestrial Globe.

May Heaven make YOUR MAJESTIES' days and reign long and prosperous, as surely as I live and die YOUR REGAL MAJESTIES'

most humble and most faithful

servant and subject

CARL LINNAEUS

To the Well-disposed Reader

MAN as a sentient being contemplates the WORLD as the theatre of the Almighty, everywhere adorned with the greatest wonders of All-knowing wisdom, and he has been brought into it as a kind of Guest so that, whilst taking pleasure in these delights, he should acknowledge the greatness of the Lord. Unworthy to be accepted as guest would be one who, in the manner of cattle, attended only to his gullet and knew not how to admire and value the mighty works of his host.

In order to go forth as GUESTS worthy of our world, we must examine carefully these works of the Creator, which the supreme Being has in such a manner bound up with our well-being that we need not lack any good things, and the more we understand these, the more they yield for the use of humanity.

Properly to acquire a KNOWLEDGE of these, it is necessary to link together a single distinct *concept* and a distinct *name*, for by neglecting this the abundance of objects would overwhelm us and all exchange of information would cease through lack of a common language.

Hence NATURAL SCIENCE was born among men, embracing under *Physics* and *Chemistry* the elements, under *Zoology, Botany* and *Mineralogy* the three realms of Nature.

It is my pleasure here to take BOTANY as my special study, which previously was the knowledge of a few plants; to-day however the abundance of material for choice has made it the most extensive of all [the sciences].

To the unwearied efforts of DISCOVERERS in recent times, among whom are especially to be named *Clusius (L'Ecluse), Columna (Colonna), the Bauhins, Hermann, Rheede, Sherard, Ray, Plukenet, Tournefort, Plumier, Vaillant, Dillenius, Gmelin* etc., we own our knowledge of many more plants than to the learned of ancient times.

KNOWLEDGE of plants formerly consisted of [knowing] arbitrary Names impressed on the tablets of *memory*, the waverings of which were mitigated by illustrations.

The wisdom of SYSTEMATISTS searched out an arrangement to help the memory and built the science on solid foundations, which we owe to the Outstanding Men *Gesner, Cesalpino, Bauhin, Morison, Hermann, Tournefort, Vaillant, Dillenius* and others.

The ARIADNEAN thread of the Systematists ended with the *Genera*. I have tried to extend it to the *Species*, having devised proper differential characters, so that certainty even in these might be established, since *all true knowledge rests upon a knowledge of the Species*; and if this is lacking, the record becomes uncertain, as in several narratives by *Travellers*.

To become well acquainted with the SPECIES of plants, I have travelled through the mountains (Alpes) of *Lapland*, all *Sweden*; parts of *Norway, Denmark, Germany*, the *Netherlands, England, France*; have after that diligently searched the botanic GARDENS of *Paris, Oxford, Chelsea, Hartekamp, Leyden, Utrecht, Amsterdam, Uppsala* and other places; have also consulted the HERBARIA of *Burser, Hermann, Clifford, Burman, Gronovius, Royen, Sloane, Sherard, Bobart, Miller, Surian, Tournefort, Vaillant, Jussieu, Bäck* and others. At my instigation my most cherished one-time STUDENTS have gone abroad, *P. Kalm* to Canada, *F. Hasselquist* to Egypt, *P. Osbeck* to China, *P. Löfling* to Spain, *Montin* to Lapland, and have sent me the plants gathered. Moreover from various countries my BOTANICAL FRIENDS have sent me not a few seeds and dried plants, notably *B. Jussieu, Royen, J. Gesner, Wachendorf, Sibthorp, Monti, Gleditsch, Krascheninnikow, Minuart, Velez*, as well as Baron *O. Munchhausen*, Baron *S. C. Bielke*, Ritter *J. Rathgeb*, Nobleman *Demidoff, Collinson, Torèn, Braad* and others. *Clifford* gave me all that he had in duplicate; *Lagerström* many from the East Indies; *Gronovius* many Virginian and *Gmelin* pretty well all Siberian, and *Sauvages* his entire collection of plants, a rare and unheard of act, whereby I have acquired no ordinary wealth of plants.

Before now I have set out the specific DIFFERENTIAL CHARACTERS for not a few plants in the *Flora Lapponica, Flora Suecica* and *Flora Zeylanica* and in the *Hortus Cliffortianus* and *Hortus Upsaliensis*. The outstanding Botanists *Gronovius, Royen, Wachendorf, Gorter, B. Jussieu, Le Monnier, Guettard, Dalibard, Sauvages, Colden* and *Hill* have adopted the same principles, as have to some degree *Haller, Gmelin* and others, through whose works many species have been made evident and settled.

These widely scattered NAMES I have planned to bring together for the sake of students, adding plants since acquired, and reducing all to one system; through many more *Species* being observed, more outstanding *marked characters* being detected and more apt *Terms* being coined, I have had sometimes to amend the differential characters, excellent though they were hitherto.

To determine the essential characters for the SPECIFIC NAME is no light task; indeed it demands an accurate knowledge of many *Species*, a most scrupulous investigation of their *parts*, the choice of *different characters*, and then the proper use of *Terminology*, that they may be expressed most concisely and surely.

I have omitted here the PLANTS NOT SEEN, being many times deceived by authors, so as not to mix the doubtful ones with those quite certain; if indeed on occasion I have been unable sufficiently to examine a plant or have obtained an imperfect specimen, I have marked this with the sign †, that others may examine the same more accurately.

Plants not named in this little book (Libellus), if any one sends them to me, I shall list in the next edition, God willing, with honorable mention of the giver.

That the NUMBER of plants of the whole world is much less than is commonly believed I ascertained by fairly safe calculation, in as much as it hardly reaches 10,000.

I have put TRIVIAL names in the margin so that without more ado we can represent one plant by one name; these I have taken, it is true, without special choice, leaving this for another day. However, I would warn most solemnly all sensible botanists not to propose a trivial name without adequate specific distinction, lest the science falls back into its early crude state.

For EUROPEAN plants I have included very few SYNONYMS, being content with *C. Bauhin* and an outstanding *Illustrator*; for EXOTICS, however, several, because they are more difficult and less familiar.

Only in doubtful instances was it necessary to add DESCRIPTIONS, and these without uncertainties, in order to keep the handbook suitable for beginners.

The original PLACE of growth I have added in my usual manner, and for the best known I have indicated *Shrubby Plants* by ♄ , *Perennials* ♃ , *Biennials* ♂, *Annuals* ☉.

I have employed (or added) some *new* GENERA, some *unchanged*, which it is my intention to put forward very soon in the new edition of the Genera plantarum.

The darts of ADVERSARIES I have never cast back; with an undisturbed mind I endured the most bitter abuse, accusations, jeers and trumpeting (in every age the rewards of labour for the most outstanding Men), and I do not envy their authors if they thereby receive greater glory from the crowd. I put up with this without turning a hair, and why should I not bear with it from the unjust, I who am overladen with the highest praises by genuine and indeed most accomplished Botanists to whom my adversaries must defer. Neither my heavy-growing years nor the position I hold, nor my character allow me to give my adversaries like for like. What of brief life remains for me I shall devote in calmness to more useful observations. The things of nature truly follow their own laws, so that just as errors regarding them cannot be defended by anybody, so truths resting upon observations cannot be trampled under foot even by the whole world of the learned; therefore I call upon our grandchildren to be the judges:

> *Envy feeds upon the living, after death is stilled,*
> *Then honour watches over a man according to his merit.*

Written the 2nd of May, 1753 at Uppsala.

12.5 T. Bergman, 'Observations on electricity, and on a thunder-storm', *Phil. Trans.*, 1761, 53, p. 705 [Abridged edition]

With regard to the electrical experiments with island crystal, given by Mr. Delaval, in the Philo. Trans., vol. 52, p. 355, Mr. B. here states, that after often repeating those experiments, he always found a contrary result. Thus, he exposed various pieces of this crystal to 12 degrees of cold of the Swedish thermometer, filled with quicksilver, being the degrees of cold below the freezing point of water, of which there are 100 between the freezing and boiling points of water. He then rubbed it after the space of some hours, but without producing any except a very small degree of electricity. Next day he repeated the experiment with a greater degree of cold, but with still less success. He next heated a small piece, hoping thus to eradicate its whole force; but unexpectedly he found its electric virtue not at all destroyed, but much increased. This being found to be the case with all the specimens he could collect, he suspects there are different kinds of this crystal, endued with such different properties. And indeed Mr. Delaval had said as much in his paper.

The thunder-storm happened at Upsal, Aug. 24, 1760; but there is nothing very remarkable in the account.

12.6 P. Wargentin, 'Observations on the same transit [of Venus]; and on an eclipse of the moon', *Phil. Trans.*, 1761, 53, pp. 560–2 [Abridged edition]

XXXVIII. Observations on the same Transit; and on an Eclipse of the Moon, May 8, and of the Sun, June 3, 1761. By Mr. Peter Wargentin, F.R.S., and Sec. R. Acad. of Sciences, Sweden. From the Latin. p. 208.

Mr. W. says the lat. of Stockholm, his situation, is 59° 20′ 31″, and its long. east of Greenwich 1^h 12^m 1^s.

A Total Eclipse of the Moon observed May 18, 1761.

At	9^h 21^m 30^s	A dense penumbra in the moon's margin.
	9 32 30	Beginning of the true eclipse.
	10 41 0	Total immersion of the moon.
	12 15 0	Beginning of the true emersion.
	13 21 8	End of the true eclipse.
	13 23 0	End of the penumbra.

A Solar Eclipse observed June 5, 1761.

| At 3^h 0^m 0^s | Sun rose eclipsed. |
| 3 12 32 | The end as much as could be seen. |

The Transit of Venus over the Sun, June 6, in the Morning.

At 3^h 21^m 37^s	Some part of Venus on the sun.
3 39 23	Interior contact, or total immersion.
9 30 8	Beginning of emersion, or interior contact.
9 48 9	End of the emersion, or exterior contact.

The beginning of the first contact could not be taken, on account of the undulation of the sun's border. The observations were made with a tube of 20 Swedish feet, of 3 inches focal distance. It was remarkable that on the exit, when a part of Venus was quite emerged, it was visible faintly illuminated. But whether this was owing to an inflection of the sun's rays, or to a refraction in the atmosphere of Venus, he leaves to others to determine.

XXXIX. An Account of the Observations made on the same Transit in Sweden. In a Letter from Mr. Peter Wargentin. Translated from the French. p. 213.

At Torneo in Lapland, Messrs. Lagerborn and Hellant very happily observed both the entrance and exit of Venus, with telescopes of 32 and 20 feet focal lengths. The principal times observed were as follow:

	Exterior contact at the entrance.	Interior contact at the entrance.	Interior contact at the exit.	Total exit.
Lagerborn	3^h 45^m 44^s	4^h 4^m 1^s	9^h 54^m 22^s	10^h 12^m 18^s
Hellant	3 45 51	4 3 59	9 54 8	10 12 22

Mr. Hellant is esteemed a very good observer. The difference between the meridians of Paris and Torneo is computed to be 1^h 27^m 28^s, very nearly.

At Abo, the capital of Finland, situated in latitude 60° 27′, longitude east of Paris 1^h 19^m 17^s, Mr. Justander observed with a telescope of 20 feet;

The interior contact, at the entrance, to be at	3^h 55^m 50^s
Beginning of the exit, at	9 46 59
Total emersion, at	10 4 42

At Hernosand, a city in Sweden, in latitude 60° 38′ and longitude 1^h 2^m 12^s east of the meridian of Paris, Messrs. Gister and Strom observed, with telescopes of 20 feet.

	h	m	s									
Mr. Gister				3^h 38^m 26^s		9^h 29^m 21^s		9^h 46^m 40^s		
Mr. Strom	3	20	40	3	38	35	..	..	..	9	46	47

At the observatory at Upsal, Messrs Stromer, Metlander Mallet, and Bergman, made the following observations, with three telescopes of 20 feet, and a reflector of 18 inches. The difference of meridians between Upsal and Paris is 1^h 1^m 10^s.

Mr. Mallet	3^h 20^m 45^s			3^h 37^m 56^s			9^h 28^m 3^s			9^h 46^m 29^s		
Mr. Stromer	..	..	..	3	38	5	9	28	7	9	46	13
Mr. Bergman	..	..	..	3	37	43	9	28	9	9	46	30

At Lund in Scanie, Mr. Schenmark observed, with a telescope of 21 feet, the interior contact of the exit was 9^h 10^m 44^s, doubtful, being cloudy; total emersion 9^h 29^m 14^s. This city is 43' 50" to the east of the meridian of Paris.

According to the observations made at the observatory at Stockholm, by Mr. Klingenstiern and Mr. Wargentin;

	h	m	s									
Mr. Klingenstiern				3^h 39^m 29^s			9^h 30^m 11^s			9^h 48^m 8^s		
Mine	3	21	37	3	39	23	9	30	8	9	48	9

The difference of meridians between Paris and Stockholm is 1^h 2^m 50^s or 52^s at most.

In these observations, Mr. W. made use of an excellent telescope, of 21 Swedish feet, and Mr. Klingenstiern observed with one of Mr. Dollond's telescopes; of 10 feet, with an eye-glass fitted to it, which magnified the object more than 140 times.

In comparing these observations together, you will perceive that they do not agree so near as was hoped for; and those which were made at Paris agree but little better.

12.7 C. W. Scheele, *Chemische Abhandlung von der Luft und dem Feuer*, Uppsala, 1777, trans. L. Dobbin. Alembic Club Reprint no. 8, 1952, pp. 5–15. Edinburgh

1. It is the object and chief business of chemistry to skilfully separate substances into their constituents, to discover their properties, and to compound them in different ways.

How difficult it is, however, to carry out such operations with the greatest accuracy, can only be unknown to one who either has never undertaken this occupation, or at least has not done so with sufficient attention.

2. Hitherto chemical investigators are not agreed as to how many elements or fundamental materials compose all substances. In fact this is one of the most difficult problems; some indeed hold that there remains no further hope of searching out the elements of substances. Poor comfort for those who feel their greatest pleasure in the investigation of natural things! Far is he mistaken, who endeavours to confine chemistry, this noble science, within such narrow bounds! Others believe that earth and phlogiston are the things from which all material nature has derived its origin. The majority seem completely attached to the peripatetic elements.

3. I must admit that I have bestowed no little trouble upon this matter in order to obtain a clear conception of it. One may reasonably be amazed at the numerous ideas and conjectures which authors have recorded on the subject, especially when they give a decision respecting the fiery phenomenon; and this very matter was of the greatest importance to me. I perceived the necessity of a knowledge of fire, because without this it is not possible to make any experiment; and without fire and heat it is not possible to make use of the action of any solvent. I began accordingly to put aside all explanations of fire; I undertook a multitude of experiments in order to fathom this beautiful phenomenon as fully as possible I soon found, however, that one could not form any true judgment regarding the phenomena which fire presents, without a knowledge of the air. I saw, after carrying out a series of experiments, that air really enters into the mixture of fire, and with it forms a constituent of flame and of sparks. I learned accordingly that a treatise like this, on fire, could not be drawn up with proper completeness without taking the air also into consideration.

4. Air is that fluid invisible substance which we continually breathe, which surrounds the whole surface of the earth, is very elastic, and possesses weight. It is always filled with an astonishing quantity of all kinds of exhalations, which are so finely subdivided in that they are scarcely visible even in the sun's rays. Water vapours always have the preponderance amongst these foreign particles. The air, however, is also mixed with another elastic substance resembling air, which differs from it in numerous properties, and is, with good reason, called aerial acid by Professsor Bergman. It owes its presence to organised bodies, destroyed by putrefaction or combustion.

5. Nothing has given philosophers more trouble for some years than just this delicate acid or so-called fixed air. Indeed it is not surprising that the conclusions which one draws from the properties of this elastic acid are not favourable to all who are prejudiced by previously conceived opinions. These defenders of the Paracelsian doctrine believe that the air is in itself unalterable; and, with Hales, that it really unites with substances thereby losing its elasticity; but that it regains its original nature as soon as it is driven out of these by fire or fermentation. But since they see that the air so produced is endowed with properties quite different from common air, they conclude, without experimental proofs, that this air has united with foreign materials, and that it must be purified from these admixed foreign particles by agitation and filtration with various liquids. I believe that there would be no hesitation in accepting this opinion, if one could only demonstrate clearly by experiments that a given quantity of air is capable of being completely converted into fixed or other kind of air by the admixture of foreign materials; but since this has not been done, I hope I do not err if I assume as many kinds of air as experiment reveals to me. For when I have collected an elastic fluid, and observe concerning it that its expansive power is increased by heat and diminished by cold, while it still uniformly retains its elastic fluidity, but also discover in it properties and behaviour different from those of common air, then I consider myself justified in believing that this is a peculiar kind of air. I say that air thus collected must retain its elasticity even in the greatest cold, because otherwise an innumerable multitude of varieties of air would have to be assumed, since it is very probable that all substances can be converted by excessive heat into a vapour resembling air.

6. Substances which are subjected to putrefaction or to destruction by means of fire diminish, and at the same time consume, a part of the air; sometimes it happens that they perceptibly increase the bulk of the air, and sometimes finally that they neither increase nor diminish a given quantity of air—phenomena which are certainly remarkable. Conjectures can here determine nothing with certainty, at least they can only bring small satisfaction to a chemical philosopher, who must have his proofs in his hands. Who does not see the necessity of making experiments in this case, in order to obtain light concerning this secret of nature?

7. General properties of ordinary air

(1.) Fire must burn for a certain time in a given quantity of air. (2.) If, so far as can be seen, this fire does not produce during combustion any fluid resembling air, then, after the fire has gone out of itself, the quantity of air must be diminished between a third and a fourth part. (3.) It must not unite with common water. (4.) All kinds of animals must live for a certain time in a confined quantity of air. (5.) Seeds, as for example peas, in a given quantity of similarly confined air, must strike roots and attain a certain height with the aid of some water and of a moderate heat.

Consequently, when I have a fluid resembling air in its external appearance, and find that it has not the properties mentioned, even when only one of them is wanting, I feel convinced that it is not ordinary air. [. . .]

19. Third Experiment.—I placed 3 teaspoonfuls of iron filings in a bottle capable of holding 2 ounces of water; to this I added an ounce of water, and gradually mixed with them half an ounce of oil of vitriol. A violent heating and fermentation too place. When the froth had somewhat subsided, I fixed into the bottle an accurately fitting cork, through which I had previously fixed a glass tube A (Fig. 1). I placed this bottle in a vessel filled with hot water, B B (cold water would greatly retard the solution). I then approached a burning candle to the orifice of the tube, whereupon the inflammable air took fire and burned with a small yellowish-green flame. As soon as this had taken place, I took a small flask C, which was capable of holding 20 ounces of water, and held it so deep in the water that the little flame stood in the middle of the flask. The water at

once began to rise gradually into the flask, and when the level had reached the point D the flame went out. Immediately afterwards the water began to sink again, and was entirely driven out of the flask. The space in the flask up to D contained 4 ounces, therefore the fifth part of the air had been lost. I poured a few ounces of lime water into the flask in order to see whether any aerial acid had also been produced during the combustion, but I did not find any. I made the same experiment with zinc filings, and it proceeded in every way similarly to that just mentioned. I shall demonstrate the constituents of this inflammable air further on; for, although it seems to follow from these experiments that it is only phlogiston, still other experiments are contrary to this.

We shall now see the behaviour of air towards that kind of fire which gives off, during the combustion, a fluid resembling air.

12.8 E. D. Clarke, *Travels in various parts of Europe, Asia and Africa*, Part 3, vol. 11, 1824, pp. 8–10, 42–7, 126–30. London

Afterwards we saw the Chemical Schools in the house of Professor *John Afzelius*, brother of *Adam Afzelius* the botanist, whom we had before visited. He was delivering a lecture, at the time of our arrival, to about twenty or thirty students; but in a voice so low and inaudible, as to be scarcely intelligible, even to those who were his constant hearers. We observed a few among them making notes; but the chief part of the audience seemed to be very inattentive, and to be sitting rather as a matter of form than for any purpose of instruction. Their slovenly dress, and manner, were moreover so unlike that of the students in our *English* Universities, that it was impossible to consider them as gentlemen: they had rather the air and appearance of so many labouring artificers, and might have been mistaken for a company of workmen in a manufactory. Around this chemical lecture-room was arranged the Professor's collection of minerals,—

perhaps more worthy of notice than any thing else in *Upsala*; for the Chemical Laboratory scarcely merits attention. It was classed according to the methodical distribution of *Cronstedt*, and has been in the possession of the University ever since the middle of the eighteenth century. The celebrated *Bergmann* added considerably to this collection, which may be considered as one of the most complete in Europe; especially in specimens from the *Swedish* mines, which have long produced the most remarkable minerals in the world. One cabinet alone contained three thousand specimens; and the whole series occupied no less a number than forty. It is true, that, in this immense collection, there were many things denoting an earlier period in the history of mineralogy, and which now belong rather to the study of *geology* than of *mineralogy*. One small cabinet contained models of mining apparatus; pumps, furnaces, &c. There is no country that has afforded better proofs of the importance of mineralogical studies to the welfare of a nation, than *Sweden*; but the *Swedes* have not maintained the pre-eminence in *mineralogy* which they so honourably acquired[1]. The *mineralogy* of *Cronstedt* laid the true foundation of the science, by making the chemical composition of minerals the foundation of the species into which they are divided[2]: and whenever an undue regard for the mere external characters of these bodies causes an attention to their chemical constituents to be disregarded, it may be regretted, as an effectual bar to the progress of mineralogical knowledge. [. . .]

It may be urged, and with truth, that public drinking-cellars are not the places in which to look for the reading class of the students: men seriously disposed towards studious employment are seldom those, in any University, who are seen in the streets or in taverns: but there was no such individual to be found in the place as a student distinguished by his talents and by his attention to University studies; and for this plain reason, that there were none of those public examinations, and those trials of ability, with distribution of honours and rewards, which powerfully call emulation into action; stimulating that love of fame inherent in every human breast, especially in youth; and feeding the fire of genius, by agitating every latent spark, until it bursts into flame. It cannot be expected, that in a society like that of *Upsala*, destitute alike of discipline and of all the springs of mental energy, its students will ever become much distinguished. [. . .]

If the Professor be a favourite, the cry of '*vivat!*' is heard, and he is suffered to proceed without molestation; but if otherwise, a shout of '*pereat!*' is the signal for attack; when the Professor either makes his escape as rapidly as he can, or is very roughly handled. There is no account taken, as in our Universities, of

---

[1] Mr. *Cripps* succeeded in purchasing copies of some of them; such as, a machine upon an improved plan for denchering land; and models of some of the *Swedish* stoves for heating apartments.

[2] The last was discovered by Dr. *Wollaston*, in some of the *iron* ore which was brought from *Lapland*. Zircon was discovered in *iron* ore by Mr. *Swedenstierna of Stockholm*. (See *Thomson's Trav. in Sweden*, p. 105. *Lond.* 1813). In some of the *iron* ore of *Gellivara*, crystals of *zircon* might be discerned.

the hours when they return to their lodgings. Every one acts as he thinks proper in this respect. Discipline, if ever any such regulation existed in *Upsala*, has long ceased; and in the total laxity of all wholesome restraint among a set of untamed youths let loose from their parents, it may be imagined what disorders must ensue. Indeed it was much to be feared at this time, and the event has in some degree justified the apprehension, that this famous University, called, by *Stillingfleet*, 'that great and hitherto unrivalled School of Natural History', together with the Empire it no longer adorned, were hastening to their dissolution. The number of students has been said to vary annually from six hundred to a thousand, which is a gross exaggeration of the truth: their number at this time, as was before stated, did not exceed three hundred; and no instance occurs of more than thirty being present at the same time at any public lecture. [. . .]

With regard to other articles of trade, the inferiority of the *Swedish* workmanship, and in many instances the total want of the article itself, is very striking. A whole day may be lost in inquiring for the most common necessaries. Of all things for which a traveller may have need, we thought that furs might be obtained here in the greatest perfection, and at the most reasonable prices; but even this branch of trade seemed to be almost a monopoly in the hands of the *English*. The best furs were all imported from *England*, and came, as it was said, originally from *America*; consequently the prices were very high, and the articles rare. All optical instruments were the wares of those vagrant *Italians* from the *Milanese* territory, whom we have before described as wandering with the proofs of their industry and ingenuity in every part of *Europe*.

It is difficult to reconcile this want of manufactures with the inventive genius shewn by the *Swedes* in one of the most pleasing of the public exhibitions of their capital—that of the *Cabinet of Models*. This cabinet is preserved in an antient palace, where the courts of justice are now held, near *Riddarholm* Church. As a repository of the models of all kinds of mechanical contrivances, it is the most complete collection that is known. We went several times to view it; and would gladly have brought to *England* specimens of the many useful inventions there shewn. In this chamber, it is not only the number of the models that strikes the spectator, but their great beauty and the exquisite perfection of the workmanship, added to the neatness with which they are arranged and displayed. Every thing necessary to illustrate the art of agriculture in *Sweden* may be here studied;—models of all the ploughs used in all the provinces from *Smoland* to *Lapland*; machines for chopping straw, for cutting turf to cover houses, for sawing timber, for tearing up the roots of trees in the forests, and for draining land; stoves for warming apartments, and for drying all sorts of fruit; machines for threshing corn; corn-racks; windmills; pumps; all sorts of mining apparatus; fishing-tackle; nets; fire-ladders; beds and chairs for the sick; in short, models of almost every mechanical aid requisite for the comforts and necessaries of life, within doors or without. There can be no doubt but that patents would be required for some of them, if they were known in *England*: and possibly patents may have been granted for inventions that were borrowed from the models in this chamber. Among them are models for light-houses, telegraphs, and other methods of making signals.

Upon this our second visit to *Stockholm*, we again examined the collection of minerals belonging to the Crown; and were much indebted to the celebrated chemist *Hjelm*, for the readiness he always shewed to gratify our curiosity; allowing us to inspect all the produce of the *Swedish* mines. The refractory nature of some of the richest *iron* ores of this country and of *Lapland* is owing to the presence of several remarkable extraneous bodies; among which may be mentioned *titanium, zircon,* and *phosphate of lime.* We had made a large collection of these ores, and the nature of them is now well ascertained. In the account we gave of our first visit to this collection, a specimen was slightly alluded to, exhibiting a remarkable prismatic configuration, taken from the bottom of a furnace in *Siberia.* How it was brought to *Stockholm* we did not learn. Some of the *Swedish* mineralogists attached more importance to this artificial appearance than we did; considering it as a satisfactory elucidation of the origin of what is commonly called the *basaltic* formation by means of igneous fusion.

Chapter 13: Science in orthodox Europe

13.1 *Letters of Euler to a German Princess*; trans. Henry Hunter, 1795

LETTER XVIII.

Difficulties attending the System of Emanation.

HOWEVER strange the doctrine of the celebrated *Newton* may appear, that rays proceed from the sun, by a continual emanation, it has, however, been so generally received, that it requires an effort of courage to call it in question. What has chiefly contributed to this, is, no doubt, the high reputation of the great English philosopher, who first discovered the true laws of the motions of the heavenly bodies: and it is this very discovery which led him to the system of emanation.

Descartes, in order to support his theory, was under the necessity of filling the whole space of the heavens with a subtile matter, through which all the celestial bodies move at perfect liberty. But it is well known, that if a body moves in air, it must meet with a certain degree of resistance; from which *Newton* concluded, that, however subtile the matter of the heavens may be supposed, the planets must encounter some resistance in their motions. But, said he, this motion is not subject to any resistance: the immense space of the heavens, therefore, contains no matter. A perfect vacuum, then, universally prevails. This is one of the leading doctrines of the Newtonian philosophy, that the immensity of the universe contains no matter, in the spaces not occupied by the heavenly bodies. This being laid down, there is between the sun and us, or at least from the sun down to the atmosphere of the earth, an absolute vacuum. In truth, the farther we ascend, the more subtile we find the air to be; from whence it would apparently follow, that at length the air would be entirely lost. If the space between the sun and the earth be an absolute vacuum, it is impossible that the rays should reach us in the way of communication, as the sound of a bell is transmitted by means of the air. For if the air, intervening between the bell and our ear, were to be annihilated, we should absolutely hear nothing, let the bell be struck ever so violently.

Having established, then, a perfect vacuum between the heavenly bodies, there remains no other opinion to be adopted, but that of emanation: which obliged *Newton* to maintain, that the sun, and all other luminous bodies, emit rays, which are always particles, infinitely small, of their mass, darted from them with incredible force. It must be such to a very high degree, in order to impress on rays of light that inconceivable velocity with which they come from the sun to us, in the space of eight minutes. But let us see whether this theory be consistent

127

with Newton's leading doctrine, which requires an absolute vacuum in the heavens, that the planets may encounter no manner of resistance to their motions. You must conclude on a moment's reflection, that the space in which the heavenly bodies revolve, instead of remaining a vacuum, must be filled with the rays, not only of the sun, but likewise of all the other stars which are continually passing through it, from every quarter, and in all directions, with incredible rapidity. The heavenly bodies which traverse these spaces, instead of encountering a vacuum, will meet with the matter of luminous rays in a terrible agitation, which must disturb these bodies in their motions, much more than if it were in a state of rest.

Thus *Newton*, apprehensive lest a subtile matter, such as *Descartes* imagined, should disturb the motions of the planets, had recourse to a very strange expedient, and quite contradictory to his own intention, as, on his hypothesis, the planets must be exposed to a derangement infinitely more considerable. I have already submitted to you several other insuperable objections to the system of emanation; and we have now seen that the principal, and indeed the only reason, which could induce *Newton* to adopt it, is so self-contradictory as wholly to overturn it. All these considerations united, leave us no room to hesitate about the rejection of this strange system of the emanation of light, however respectable the authority of the philosopher who invented it.

Newton was, without doubt, one of the greatest geniuses that ever existed. His profound knowledge, and his acute penetration into the most hidden mysteries of nature, will be a just object of admiration to the present, and to every future age. But the errors of this great man should serve to admonish us of the weakness of the human understanding, which, after having soared to the greatest possible heights, is in danger of plunging into manifest contradiction.

If we are liable to weaknesses and inconsistences so humiliating, in our researches into the phenomena of this visible world, which lies open to the examination of our senses, how wretched must we have been, had God left us to ourselves with respect to things invisible, and which concern our eternal salvation? On this important article, a Revelation was absolutely necessary to us; and we ought to avail ourselves of it, with the most profound veneration. When it presents to us things which may appear inconceivable, we have but to reflect on the imperfection of human understanding, which is so apt to be misled, even as to sensible objects. Whenever I hear a pretended Freethinker inveighing against the truths of religion, and even sneering at it with the most arrogant, self-sufficiency, I say to myself: poor weak mortal, how inexpressibly more noble and sublime are the subjects which you treat so lightly, than those respecting which the great *Newton* was so grossly mistaken! I could wish your Highness to keep this reflection ever in remembrance: occasions for making it occur but too frequently.

LETTER LXXXIX.

Of the Question respecting the best World possible; and of the Origin of Evil.

You know well, that it has been made a question, Whether this world be the best possible? It cannot be doubted, that the world perfectly corresponds to the plan which God proposed to himself, when he created it.

As to bodies, and material productions, their arrangement and structure are such, that certainly they could not have been better. Please to recollect the wonderful structure of the eye, and you will see the necessity of admitting, that the conformation of all its parts is perfectly adapted to fulfil the end in view, that of representing distinctly exterior objects. How much address is necessary to keep up the eye in that state, during the course of a whole life? The juices which compose it must be preserved from corruption; it was necessary to make provision, that they should be constantly renewed, and maintained in a suitable state.

A structure equally marvellous is observable in all the other parts of our bodies, in those of all animals, and even of the vilest insects. [. . .]

We discover the same perfection in plants: every thing in them concurs to their formation, to their growth, and to the production of their flowers, of their fruits, or of their seeds. What a prodigy to behold a plant, a tree, spring from a small grain, cast into the earth, by the help of the nutritious juices with which the soil supplies it? The productions found in the bowels of the earth are no less wonderful: every part of nature is capable of exhausting our utmost powers of research, without permitting us to penetrate all the wonders of its construction. Nay, we are utterly lost, while we reflect, how every substance, earth, water, air, and fire, concur in the production of all organized bodies; and, finally, how the arrangement of all the heavenly bodies is so admirably contrived, as perfectly to fulfil all these particular destinations.

After having reflected in this manner, it will be difficult for you to believe, that there should have been men who maintained, that the universe was the effect of mere chance, without any design. But there always have been, and there still are, persons of this description; those, however, who have a solid knowledge of nature, and whom fear of the justice of God does not prevent from acknowledging Him, are convinced, with us, that there is a Supreme Being, who created the whole universe, and, from the remarks which I have just been suggesting to you, respecting bodies, every thing has been created in the highest perfection.

13.2 S. P. Krasheninnikov, *The History of Kamtschatka;* trans. by James Grieve, from *Opisanie zemli Kamchatki,* 1764 [Extracts]

The *Kamtschadales* esteem all the burning mountains, and places where hot springs arise, as the habitations of spirits, and approach them with fear; but, as the latter are the most dangerous, they are under the greatest awe of them; and therefore they never willingly discover them to any *Russian*, lest they should be obliged to accompany him near them. It was by chance that I heard of them after I had travelled 100 versts from the place; but this natural phænomenon appeared so curious that I returned to examine it. The people of *Shematchinski* village were obliged to declare the true reason why they had not formerly discovered them, and much against their will were forced to shew me the place, but would not go near it: and when they saw that we lay in the water, drank it, and eat things boiled with it, they expected to see us perish immediately; but when they perceived this did not happen, they told it in the village as an uncommon wonder, and looked upon us as very extraordinary people, since even the devils could not hurt us. [. . .]

The wild garlick is not only useful in the kitchen, but also in medicine. Both the *Russians* and *Kamtschadales* gather great quantities, which they cut and dry in the sun for their winter provision; at which time boiling it in water they ferment it a little, and use it as an herb soup, which they call *shami*. They esteem the wild garlick so efficacious a remedy against the scurvy, that they think themselves in no danger so soon as it begins to shew itself under the snow: and I have heard an extraordinary account of its virtues from the Cossacks that were employed with captain *Spanberg* in building the sloop Gabriel: they were so ill with the scurvy, that scarce any were able to work, or even to walk, so long as the ground was covered with snow; but as soon as the high lands began to appear green, and the wild garlick to sprout out, the Cossacks fed upon it greedily. Upon their first eating it, they were covered over with scabs in such a manner, that the captain believed they were all infected with the venereal disease. In about a fortnight, these scabs fell off, and they were perfectly recovered of the scurvy. [. . .]

Some call the sea lions sea horses, because they have manes. In their shape they are like the sea calf; and their necks are bare, excepting a small mane of hard curled hairs: the rest of their body is covered with a chesnut-coloured hair. They have a middle-sized head, short ears, a snout short and drawn up like a pug dog's, great teeth, and webbed feet. They are found most frequently about rocky shores or rocks in the sea, upon which they climb very high, in great numbers. They roar in a strange, frightful manner, much louder than the sea calf; and they are thus far of use to people at sea, that in foggy weather, by their roaring, they warn them of rocks or islands being near, as few rocks or islands in this part of the world are without these animals.

Although in appearance and size this animal seems to be very dangerous, and marches with such a fierce mien that he looks like a true lion, yet is he such a coward, that at the sight of a man he hurries into the water; and when he is surprised asleep, and awakened either by a loud cry or blows with a club, he is in such fear and confusion, that in running away he falls down, all his joints quaking with terror; but, when he finds no possibility of escaping, he will then attack his enemy with the greatest fierceness, shaking his head and roaring very terribly; and then the boldest must seek to save himself from his rage. [. . .]

Although these animals naturally run from a man, yet it has been observed that they are not always so wild; particularly when their young have scarcely learned to swim. Mr. *Steller* lived six days in a high place amongst whole herds of them, and out of his hut saw several of their actions. The animals lay around him, seeming to observe his fire and what he was employed about; and never ran away, although he even went amongst them, and seized some of their young for his dissections, but remained quite at their ease. [. . .]

Besides those already described, there are several other sea animals here, the most remarkable of which is the manati, or sea cow. This animal never comes out upon the shore, but always lives in the water; its skin is black and thick, like the bark of an old oak, and so hard that one can scarcely cut it with an ax; its head in proportion to its body is small, and falls off from the neck to the snout, which is so much bent that the mouth seems to lie below; towards the end the snout is white and rough, with white whiskers about nine inches long; it has no teeth, but only two flat white bones, one above, the other below; its nostrils are near the end of its snout, in length and breadth about an inch and a half; they are double, and within are rough and hairy; its eyes are black, placed almost in the middle, and near in one line with the nostrils, they are no larger than sheep's eyes, which is certainly remarkable in such a monstrous creature; it has no eyebrows nor eyelashes; and its ears are only a small opening; its neck is not easily discovered, the head and body being so nearly joined; however, there are some vertebræ proper for turning the head upon, which it actually does, particularly when it feeds, hanging its head like a cow; its body is round like that of a seal; being thickest about the navel, and growing smaller towards the head and tail; the tail is thick, and bent a little towards the end; it something resembles the beard of the whale, and somewhat the fins of a fish; its paws, which are under its neck, are about 21 inches long, with them he both swims and goes, and by them he takes hold of the rocks, to which he sometimes fastens himself so strongly, that when he is dragged from thence with hooks he will leave the skin of his paws behind: it is observed that these paws are sometimes divided in two, like the hoof of a cow; but this does not seem to be common, only accidental. The females have two teats upon their breasts. The length of the manati is about 28 feet, and its weight about 200 pood. These animals go in droves in calm weather near the mouths of rivers; and though the dams oblige their young always to swim before them, yet the rest of the herd cover them upon all sides, so that they are constantly in the middle of the drove. In the time of flood they come so near the shore, that one may strike them with a club or spear; nay, the author relates that he has even stroked their backs himself with his hand. When they are hurt they swim off to sea, but presently return. [. . .]

They are caught with great iron hooks, something like the fluke of a small anchor. This hook is carried by a strong man in a boat with three or four rowers, who when he comes among the herd strikes into one of them. Thirty men that are left upon the shore, and hold one end of a rope which is fastened to the hook, draw the manati towards the land; and in the mean time those that are in the boat stab and cut it 'till it dies. [. . .]

There is such a plenty of manati in *Bering*'s island, that it is sufficient to maintain all the people of *Kamtschatka*. Their flesh, though it takes a long time to boil, tastes well, and is something like beef. The fat of the young resembles pork, and the lean is like veal. [. . .]

As *Kamtschatka* abounds with lakes and marshes, the swarms of insects in the summer time would make life intolerable there, if it were not for the frequent winds and rains. The maggots are so numerous as to occasion great destruction to their provisions, particularly in the time of preparing their fish, which are sometimes entirely destroyed by them. In the months of *June, July,* and *August,* when the weather happens to be fine, the musketoes and small gnats are very troublesome; however the inhabitants do not suffer much from them, as they are at that time, upon account of the fishery, out at sea, where by reason of the cold and wind few of these insects are to be met with. [. . .]

There are few spiders in *Kamtschatka*; so that the women who are fond of having children, and who have a notion that these insects swallowed render them fruitful and their labour easy, have great trouble to find them. Nothing plagues the natives in their huts so much as the lice and fleas; the women suffer most from the former, by wearing very long, and sometimes false hair. Mr. *Steller* was told, that near the sea is found an insect that resembles a louse, which working itself through the skin into the flesh is never to be cured, unless by cutting the creature intirely out; and that the fishers are very much afraid of them. [. . .]

Although in outward appearance they resemble the other inhabitants of *Siberia*, yet the *Kamtschadales* differ in this, that their faces are not so long as the other *Siberians'*, their cheeks stand more out, their teeth are thick, their mouth large, their stature middling, and their shoulders broad, particularly those people who inhabit the sea coast.

Their manner of living is slovenly to the last degree; they never wash their hands nor face, nor cut their nails; they eat out of the same dish with the dogs, which they never wash; every thing about them stinks of fish; they never comb their heads, but both men and women plait their hair in two locks, binding the ends with small ropes: when any hair starts out, they sow it with threads to make it lie close; by this means they have such a quantity of lice that they can scrape them off by handfuls, and they are nasty enough even to eat them. Those that have not natural hair sufficient wear false locks, sometimes as much as weigh ten pounds, which makes their heads look like a haycock. [. . .]

They have filled almost every place in heaven and earth with different spirits, which they both worship and fear more than God: they offer them sacrifices upon every occasion, and some carry little idols about them, or have them placed in their dwellings; but, with regard to God, they not only neglect to worship him; but, in case of troubles and misfortunes, they curse and blaspheme him.

They keep no account of their age, though they can count as far as one hundred; but this is so troublesome to them that without their fingers they do not tell three. It is very diverting to see them reckon more than ten; for having reckoned the fingers of both hands they clasp them together, which signifies ten; then they begin with their toes, and count to twenty; after which they are quite confounded, and cry, *Matcha?* that is, Where shall I take more. They reckon ten months in the year, some of which are longer and some shorter; for they do not divide them by the changes of the moon, but by the order of particular occurrences that happen in those regions. [. . .]

They do not distinguish the days by any particular appellation, nor form them into weeks or months, nor yet know how many days are in the month or year. They mark their epochs by some remarkable thing or other, such as the arrival of the *Russians*, the great rebellion, or the first expedition to *Kamtschatka*. They have no writings, nor hieroglyphick figures, to preserve the memory of any thing; so that all their knowledge depends upon tradition, which soon becomes uncertain and fabulous in regard to what is long past.

They are ignorant of the causes of eclipses, but when they happen, they carry fire out of their huts, and pray the luminary eclipsed to shine as formerly. They know only three constellations; the Great Bear, the Pleiades, and the three stars in Orion; and give names only to the principal winds. [. . .]

The burial of the dead, if one can call throwing them to the dogs a burial, is different here from what it is in any other part of the world; for instead of burning or laying the dead bodies in some hole, the *Kamtschadales* bind a strap round the neck of the corps, draw it out of the hut, and deliver it for food to their dogs: for which they give the following reasons; that those who are eaten by dogs will drive with fine dogs in the other world; and that they throw them round near the hut, that evil spirits, whom they imagine to be the occasion of their death, seeing the dead body, may be satisfied with the mischief they have done. [. . .]

As the *Koreki* and *Kuriles* agree in most of their customs and habits with the *Kamtschadales*, we shall only take notice of those things wherein they differ from them or from one another. The *Koreki*, as is above related, are divided into the rein-deer or wandering *Koreki*; and those that are fixed in one place who live in huts in the earth like the *Kamtschadales*, and in every other respect indeed resemble them; so that whatever remarks we make are to be understood of the wandering *Koreki*, unless otherwise expressed. [. . .]

There is besides a very great difference in their customs and habits. The wandering *Koreki* are extremely jealous, and sometimes kill their wives upon suspicion only; but when any are caught in adultery, both parties are certainly condemned to death. For this reason the women seem to take pains to make themselves disagreeable; for they never wash their faces or hands, nor comb their hair, and their upper garments are dirty, ragged, and torn, the best being worn underneath. This they are obliged to do on account of the jealousy of their husbands; who say, that a woman has no occasion to adorn herself unless to gain the affections of a stranger, for her husband loves her without that. On the contrary, the fixed *Koreki*, and *Tchukotskoi*, look upon it as the truest mark of friendship, when they entertain a friend, to put him to bed with their wife or daughter; and a refusal of this civility they consider as the greatest affront; and are even capable of murdering a man for such a contempt. This happened to several *Russian* Cossacks before they were acquainted with the customs of the people. The wives of the fixed *Koreki* endeavour to adorn themselves as much as possible, painting their faces, wearing fine cloaths, and using various means to set off their persons. In their huts they sit quite naked, even in the company of strangers.

13.3 Mikhail Lomonosov, *The Appearance of Venus on the Sun, observed at the St. Petersburg Academy of Sciences on the 26th Day of May in the Year 1761*. Addendum; trans. from M. V. Lomonosov, *Izbrannye proizvedeniya*, tom 1: *Estestvennye nauki i filosofiya*, 1986, pp. 333–6. Moscow: Nauka

This rarely encountered phenomenon requires a twofold explanation. First, it is necessary to dispel among uneducated people any unfounded doubts and fears, which are sometimes the cause of general unrest. Not infrequently, heads filled with credulity heed with horror prophecies made on the basis of such celestial phenomena by itinerant beggar-women, who not only have never heard of the word astronomy throughout the whole of their long lives, but can scarcely with their stooping walk glance up at the sky. The stupidity of such ignorant soothsayers and their superstitious listeners should be treated with nothing but contemptuous laughter. Anyone who is disturbed by such dire prognostications deserves his anxiety as a punishment for his own witlessness. But this pertains more to the common people, who have no understanding of the sciences. The peasant ridicules the astronomer as an empty trifler. The astronomer is inwardly amused, realizing how far in his own knowledge he surpasses a man created so like himself.

The second explanation extends to literate people, to readers of Scripture, and devotees of Orthodoxy, whose sacred concerns are laudable in themselves, even if they have sometimes through excess hindered the progress of the higher sciences.

On reading about the extensive atmosphere around the aforementioned planet described here, one of them will say that on account of it, vapours rise, clouds form, rains fall, streams run and collect into rivers, rivers flow into the sea, various plants spring up everywhere, and animals feed on them. And this, like the Copernican system, is against divine law.

Thinking like this led to a similar controversy about the mobility of the Earth. Theologians of the Western Church interpret the words of Joshua, Chapter 10, verse 12, in a precisely literal sense, and on that basis attempt to prove that the Earth is motionless.

But this controversy began not with Christian but with pagan scholars. Of the ancient astronomers (long before the birth of Christ), Nicetas of Syracuse recognized the daily rotation of the Earth about its axis, and Philolaus its annual revolution around the sun. A hundred years later, Aristarchus of Samos gave a clearer account of the solar system. However, the high priests of Hellenic superstition opposed his account, and suppressed the truth for many centuries. [. . .] Meanwhile, the astronomers were obliged to devise ridiculous cycles and epicycles (circles and subsidiary circles), contrary to the mechanics and geometry of the planets' orbits.

A pity that in those times there were no cooks as sharp-witted as the following:

> Once, feasting, two astronomers were seated,
> And argued 'mongst themselves in language heated.
> Earth turning travels round the Sun, did one maintain,
> The other that Sun leads the planets in its train.
> This one was Ptolemy, the first, Copernicus.
> The smiling Cook resolved their quarrel thus:
> Knowst thou the course of stars? the host inquired?
> Then how to solve this question art inspired?
> Copernicus was right, the answer went.
> I'll prove it true, although I've never spent
> Time on the Sun. What Cook of brains could boast
> So few, to turn the Hearth about the Roast?*

In the end, Copernicus revived the solar system, which now bears his name, and demonstrated its marvellous utility in astronomy. Afterwards, Kepler, Newton and other great mathematicians and astronomers raised it to the level of accuracy we now see in predictions of celestial phenomena, a level quite impossible to achieve using a geostatic system.

Although the untold wisdom of divine activity is apparent from the study of all His creatures, in which the physical sciences lead the way, the magnificence and power of His understanding is shown above all by astronomy, which demonstrates order in the behaviour of the heavenly bodies. We have a clearer conception of the Creator, the more closely observations match our predictions; and the better we comprehend our discoveries, the louder we glorify Him.

---

* Rhyming was taken from B. N. Menshutkin, *Russia's Lomonosov*, 1952, p. 149. Princeton University Press.

Holy Scripture should not always be understood literally, but sometimes in a rhetorical sense. St. Basil the Great gives examples of its concord with nature, and in his Homilies of the Hexaemeron clearly shows how the words of the Bible should be interpreted in such instances. [. . .] Discussing God's words and commands on the creation of the World: 'And God said' and so on, he declares as follows: 'Such words are needed for the mind itself to communicate with others' (Homily 2), clearly explaining that divine words do not require mouth, ears or breath for the communication of this goodwill, but that He holds forth by the force of intellect. And in another place (Homily 3), he makes the same point about the clarification of such passages: 'In the curses on Israel, it is said: "And thy heaven above thy head shall be brass". What does this mean? A total drought and an absence of aerial waters.' [. . .] Is it not enough that here this great and holy man has shown that the interpretation of the sacred books is not only allowed, but indeed necessary, whenever the use of metaphorical expressions leads to an apparent inconsistency with nature?

Truth and faith are two kindred sisters, the daughters of one supreme parent: there can never be any discord between them, unless some slanderer, out of vanity and in an attempt to display his own wisdom, imputes enmity to them. But reasonable and good persons must search for means to explain and avert all so-called conflict between them, following the aforementioned wise teacher of our Orthodox Church. Agreeing with him, St. John of Damascus, the profound theologian and writer of lofty religious verse, wrote. [. . .] concerning various opinions on the structure of the world: 'However, whether it is this way or some other, everything exists and is established by God's command.' That is, physical discussions about the structure of the world serve to glorify God, and are not inimical to religion. [. . .]

These great luminaries thus strove to harmonize natural science with religion, reconciling the achievements of the former with certain divinely-inspired thoughts expressed in the Bible within the limits of contemporary astronomical knowledge. If only our present astronomical instruments had been invented then, and numerous observations made by men incomparably surpassing the ancient astronomers in their knowledge of the heavenly bodies, if only thousands of new stars and other phenomena had been discovered, with what flights of spirituality and marvellous eloquence would these holy rhetoricians have preached the wisdom, power and majesty of God! [. . .]

The Creator has given the human race two books. In one, he displayed his greatness, in the other his will. The first is this visible world, created by Him so that man, observing the immensity, beauty and symmetry of his structures, should recognize divine omnipotence, within the limits of understanding granted him. The second book is the Holy Scripture. In it is shown the Creator's goodwill towards our salvation. The great church teachers are the interpreters and expounders of these divinely-inspired books of the prophets and apostles. The physicists, mathematicians, astronomers and other expounders of the divine acts influential in nature are to the book of the constitution of this visible world, what the prophets, apostles and church teachers are to the other book. The mathematician reasons incorrectly, if he wishes to measure the divine will with a pair of compasses. So does the teacher of theology, if he thinks that one can learn astronomy or chemistry from the psalter.

The interpreters and preachers of the Holy Scripture show the path to virtue, depict the rewards of the righteous, the punishment of lawbreakers and the happiness of the life which accords with the divine will. Astronomers reveal the temple of divine power and majesty, and search out means for our temporal welfare, uniting it with reverence and gratitude toward the Supreme Being. Both in general convince us not only of God's existence, but also of His untold kindness to us. [. . .]

Chapter 14: Establishing science in eighteenth-century central Europe

14.1 Robert Jameson, 'On the Supposed Existence of Mechanical Deposits and Petrefactions in the Primitive Mountains, and an Account of Petrefactions which have been discovered in the newest Flötz Trapp Formation', *Journal of Natural Philosophy, Chemistry and the Arts*, 1802 [Nicholson's Journal], 3 pp. 13–21

On the supposed Existence of Mechanical Deposits and Petrefactions in the Primitive Mountains, and an Account of Petrefactions which have been discovered in the newest Flötz Trapp Formation. By Mr. ROBERT JAMESON. Communicated by the Author.

OUR globe, according to the Wernerian geognosia, even during the decomposition of the newer primitive strata, appears to have been covered to a great height with water, as is evinced by the want of all mechanical deposit.* After the precipitation of these great rock formations, the level of the water became so low, as to allow it to act mechanically upon the subjacent rocks; this occasioned the first mechanical deposition, which discovers itself in the transition rocks (Ubergangsgebürge). Nearly at the same time organization commenced, as it is in the transition rocks we find the first traces of organic remains: these are generally zoophytes and sea plants, a fact which goes deep not only into geology, but natural history.

> The primitive rocks precipitated from a great depth of water which covered the globe.

> The transition rocks when the water was lower: at which time organization began.

Professor Playfair, in his illustrations of the Huttonian theory, mentions several instances of mechanical deposits and petrefactions which have been discovered among the primary strata, and from these he concludes, that no such series of strata as the transition exist. I shall now examine the statements he has given; and first respecting the occurrence of petrefactions in primary mountains.

> Instances of mechanical deposits in primary strata: offered by Professor Playfair.

At page 164 he observes, 'Another spot, affording instances of shells in primitive limestone, is in Devonshire, on the sea

> Shells in primitive limestone, in the

*The exception to this in the sienite formation I explained in a former paper.

vicinity of
Plymouth, &c.

shore, on the east side of Plymouth dock, opposite to
Stonehouse, I found a specimen of shistose micaceous
limestone, containing a shell of the bivalve kind; it was
struck off from the solid rock, and cannot possibly be
considered as an adventitious fossil. Now, no rocks can be
more decidedly primary than those about Plymouth; they
consist of calcareous strata, in the form either of marble or
micaceous limestone, alternating with shistus of the same
kind, which prevails through Cornwall to the west, and
extends eastward into Dartmoor, and on the sea coast as far
as Berry Head. These all intersect the horizontal plane in a
line from east to west nearly; they are very erect, those at
Plymouth being elevated to the north.' That petrefactions
exist in the limestone at Plymouth is evident; but that these
strata are primitive, still remain to be proved. The character
given of the limestone does not exclude it from the transition
strata; but of the shistus we cannot judge, as neither its
oryctognostical, or geognostical characters are given. The
other instances which are alluded to, are liable to the same
objection. I cannot therefore agree with Professor Playfair
in believing 'Though, therefore, the remains of marine
animals are not frequent among the primary rocks, they are
not excluded from them; and hence the existence of shell
fish and zoophytes, is clearly proved to be anterior to the
formation even of those parts of the present land which are
justly accounted the most ancient.'

But it is not proved
that those strata are
primitive.

Whence the
conclusion of the
Professor is not
agreed to.

The position that
vegetable matters
are found in
primitive strata need
not be examined.

Professor Playfair agrees with Dr. Hutton in affirming, that
vegetable matters occur in the primitive strata: I do not find
it necessary to enter into an examination of what they have
said upon this subject, as they have evidently confounded
a geognostical with an oryctognostical investigation.

Prof. Playfair's
proofs of mechanical
deposits in primitive
strata examined.

I shall now examine the proofs which Professor Playfair has
brought to establish the existence of mechanical deposits in
primitive strata.

Mount St. Gothard
a central primitive
mountain, has
arenaceous strata in
its vicinity

The first we meet with is from Saussure. Professor Playfair
remarks, 'St. Gothard is a central point, in one of the greatest
tracts of primary mountains on the face of the earth, yet
arenaceous strata are found in its vicinity. Between Ayrolo
and the Hospice of St. Gothard, Saussure found a rock,
composed of an arenaceous or granular paste, including in
it hornblende and garnets. He is somewhat unwilling to give
the name gres to this stone, which Mr. Besson has done;
but he nevertheless describes it as having a granulated
structure.'

The rock of Ayrolo is primitive, and is either gneiss or mica slate. Garnets are seldom found in gneiss, but are characteristic for mica slate; the geognost, therefore, would not hesitate to consider the rock here mentioned as belonging to mica slate.

Observation. The rock here mentioned was gneiss or mica slate.

Professor Playfair continues, 'Among the most indurated rocks that compose the mountains of this island, many are arenaceous. Thus, on the western coast of Scotland, the great body of high and rugged mountains on the shores of Arasaig, &c. from Ardnamurchan to Glen-elg, consists, in a great measure, of a granitic sandstone, in vertical beds. This stone sometimes occupies great tracts; at other times, it is alternated with the micaceous, and other varieties of primary shistus; it occurs, likewise, in several of the islands, and is a fossil which we hardly find described or named by writers on mineralogy.'

Instances by P. Playfair of indurated arenaceous granite.

This granitic sandstone of Glen-elg is most certainly gneiss,* and a variety which is not uncommon; and I may venture to say, that the strata in Arasaig, &c. are of the same nature.

Obs. This granitic sandstone is gneiss.

Professor Playfair concludes with stating the following examples, as a further confirmation of his opinion—'Much also of a highly indurated, but granulated quartz, is found in several places in Scotland, in beds of strata, alternated with the common shistus of the mountain. Remarkable instances of this may be seen on the north side of the ferry of Balachulish, and again on the sea shore at Cullen. At the latter, the strata are remarkably regular, alternating with different species of shistus. At the former, the quartz is so pure, that the stone has been mistaken for marble.

Other examples of Pr. Playfair. Granulated quartz in beds alternating with the shistus.

'These examples are perhaps sufficient; but I must add, that in the micaceous and talcose schisti themselves, thin layers of sand are often found interposed between the layers of mica or talc. I have seen a specimen from the summit of one of the highest of the Grampian mountains, where the thin plates, of a talcy or asbestine substance, are separated by layers of a very fine quartzy sand, not much consolidated. The mountain from which it was brought, consists of vertical strata, much intersected by quartz veins. It is impossible to doubt, in this instance, that the thin plates of the one substance, and the small grains of the other, were deposited together at the bottom of the sea, and that they were alike

Whence he concludes that they were deposited (mechanically) at the same time.

* Mineralogy of the Scottish isles, vol. ii, p. 160.

produced from the degradation of rocks more ancient than any which now exist.'

Obs. Granular quartz is not a mechanical, but a chemical deposition. For this differs from mica slate in the absence of slaty fracture; but the series between each are gradual. Mica slate differs from gneiss in wanting felspar; but here also the transition is equally gradual. And gneiss differs from granite by its slaty fracture, which it as gradually loses. The gradation from granular quartz to granite being perfect, the one is no more a mechanical deposit than the other. Loose texture is no proof of mechanical deposition; and layers of sand are found in veins which in the volcanic theory are said to bear every mark of complete fusion. General observations.

I am surprised Professor Playfair should adduce granular quartz as a proof of mechanical deposition, as it has no more claim to such a character than granite. The following observations will render this evident; granular quartz differs from mica slate, in the absence of the slaty fracture, and mica; we have, however, a series from the most complete granular quartz to the most perfect mica slate. Again, mica slate, which differs from gneiss, in wanting felspar, is to be observed in all the intermediate stages until it passes into complete gneiss; the gneiss, which is principally distinguished from granite by its slaty fracture, gradually loses this fracture, and at length is not to be distinguished from granite. Thus we have a complete gradation from the purest granular quartz to granite, and not only in hand specimens, but in the mountains themselves. It therefore follows, that if granular quartz is a mechanical deposit, so is granite, a position which I believe the Huttonian system would not allow.

That the granular quartz should occur sometimes of a very loose texture; nay, even as Professor Playfair remarks sandy, is not surprising, for in granite and basalt we have similar appearances. Even in veins, which to use Professor Playfair's own words, bear all the marks of complete fusion, layers of granular quartz, from the most compact to the looseness of sand have been observed. The great sand veins in the Hartz afford remarkable instances of this; also, as I have more lately discovered, the lead veins at Wanlock-head in Lancashire.

Account of Organic Remains which have been discovered in the newest Flötz Trapp Formation.

Many different accounts had been given of the geognostic relations of the rocks of this formation, before they engaged the attention of Werner, the great founder of *true geognosia*. After having made the remarkable discovery upon the hill of Scheibenberg, he extended his inquiries to all the basalt hills in Germany, and found in every quarter corresponding appearances. This confirmed more completely the conclusions he had then drawn, and entirely overthrew the volcanic system. He however did not stop here; his after observations disclosed a connection among these appearances, which at first he was not probably aware of; they placed the

Neptunian system beyond the reach of attack, and completely annihilated a host of hypothesis. He proved,

1. That this is the newest of all the great rock formations, of which the crust of the earth is composed.
2. That all the apparently unconnected hills and masses of this formation, have formerly stood in connection with each other.
3. That it exists in all quarters of the globe.

These facts lead him to the great discovery, that this formation at one time, extended as a cover around the whole earth. From these observations it is evident, that we may expect to meet with vestiges of many of the organic and unorganic matter which at that time existed upon the crust of the earth, in the rocks of this formation.

Accordingly, the investigations of geognosts have discovered organic remains in every rock of this formation; the following are given as instances:

Organic Remains in Greenstone, Basalt, Wacke, and Trapp Buccin.

QUADRUPEDS

1. Werner in his geognostic lectures, informs us that the wacken of Kalten-nordheim is sometimes found to contain deers horns.
2. The Abbé Fortis discovered the head of an unknown animal in a soft wacken, in the valley of Ronca in the Veronese. *Vide Beschrebbung des Thales Ronca, s. 96.*
3. Saussure observed bones of quadrupeds in the wacken of the catacombs of Rome.

Lettre a Mr. le Chev. Hamilton, J. de Physicque. Tom. VII.

SHELLS AND ZOOPHYTES

1. Dr. Richardson found shells in rocks of the Trapp formation at Ballycastle in Ireland—*Kirwan's Geol. Essays.*
2. Mr. Von Buch informs us, that in the county of Landeck, he observed a bed of wacken, which contained besides pebbles of chalcedony, turbinates in a state of complete preservation. *Versuch einer mineralogisten Veschreibung von Landeck, von Leopold von Buch, s. 35.*

Marginal notes:

Results. 1. That this is the newest of the great rocks.
2. That all the now unconnected masses of this formation were once connected.
3. That it exists everywhere.
4. That it formerly covered the whole earth, and must contain organic remains.

Organic remains in greenstone, basalt, &c. found; viz. of quadrupeds.

Of shells and zoophytes.

3. Abbé Fortis observed numerous petrefactions of shells in Wacken, and Trapp Breccia, also a few in Basalt, in the formation of the valley of Ronca.

4. Berolding found a cornu ammonis, which still retained its mother of pearl lustre, in the basalt of Torez. In the basalt of Thurgau, near the Boden lake, he observed gryphites, ammonites, and glossopetræ, *Chem. Annal.* 1794, p. 103.

5. In the Wernerian collection of petrefactions I saw specimens of greenstone, containing petrefactions of shells.

Of vegetables

VEGETABLE REMAINS

1. Werner observed great trees, with branches, leaves, and fruit, in the wacken, at Joachimsthal.

2. Friesleben describes the impression of a plant in the Kawsower Berg, near to Podsedlitz.

3. In the islands of Banna and Skye I observed pieces of wood in Trapp Breccia, and Mineralogy of the Scottish isles, vol. ii, p. 58–75.

Organic remains in slaty clay, limestone, and sandstone, of this formation. Shells.

Organic remains found in slaty clay, limestone, and **sandstone**, which belongs to the Flötz Trapp formation.

SHELLS

1. Abbé Fortis, in his account of the valley of Ronca, informs us, that limestone and slaty clay often alternate with basalt, wacken, and trapp breccia. The limestone and slaty clay contains numerous petrefactions of shells, which are of the same kinds with those found in the basalt, wacken, and trapp breccia.

2. In the island of Eigg, where there appears to be a similar formation with that of Ronca, I observed that the limestone, slaty clay, and sandstone, contained numerous petrefactions of shells. Mineralogy of the Scottish isles, vol. ii.

Of vegetables.

VEGETABLE REMAINS

1. At the northern extremity of the island of Skye,

where basalt alternates with limestone and slaty clay, I observed pieces of carbonated wood in the limestone. Mineralogy of the Scottish isles, vol. ii, p. 80.*

2. In the flinty sandstone, which usually accompanies this formation, I have observed branches of shrubs; vegetable matters that occur inveloped in rocks are generally, either carbonated or bituminated, here however they are not altered.

R. JAMESON.

Sheriff Bræ, Leith.

POSTSCRIPT

Since writing the enclosed, I have examined one of those appearances, which are considered by Dr. Hutton and Professor Playfair, as demonstrating the existence of petrefactions in primitive mountains. Dr. Hutton, at p. 334 of his Theory of the Earth, remarks, 'I have already observed, that one single example of a shell, or of its print, in a schistus, or in a stone stratified among those vertical or erected masses, suffices to prove the origin of these bodies to have been, what I had maintained them to be, water formed strata created from the bottom of the sea, like every other consolidated stratum of the earth. But now, I think, I may affirm that there is not, or rarely, any considerable extent of country of the primary kind, in which some mark of this origin will not be found, upon careful examination; and now I will give my reason for this assertion. I have been examining the south alpine country of Scotland occasionally, for forty years back, and I could not find any mark of an organized body in the schistus of those mountains. It is true, that I knew of only one place where limestone is found among the strata: this is upon Tweedside near the Crook. This quarry I had carefully examined long ago, but could find no mark of any organized body in it. I suppose they are now working some other of the vertical strata near to those which I had examined: for, in the summer of 1792, I received a letter from Sir James Hall, which I shall now transcribe. It is dated Moffat, June 2, 1792.

Dr. Hutton's statement of facts to shew the mechanical origin of primitive countries from the existence of organic remains.

---

* Mr. Kirwan, in the first volume of his System of Mineralogy, has given us an excellent account of the different opinions respecting the formation of basalt; and has adduced many arguments that shew the fallacy of the Volcanic and Plutonic hypothesis.

Sir James Hall's
account of organic
remains in a
limestone stated to
be primitive.

'As I was riding yesterday between Noble House and the
Crook, on the road to this place, I fell in with a quarry of
alpine limestone; it consists of four or five strata, about three
feet thick, one of them single, and the rest contiguous; they
all stand between the strata of slate and schist, that are at
that place nearly vertical. In the neighbourhood, a slate
quarry is worked of pure blue slate; several of the strata of
slate near the limestone, are filled with fragments of limestone
scattered about like the fragments of schist in the sandstone,
in the neighbourhood of the junction on our coast. Among
the masses of limestone lately broken off for use, and having
the fracture fresh, I found the forms of cockles quite distinct,
and in great abundance. I send you three pieces of this kind,'
&c.

It may perhaps be alleged, that those mountains of Cumber-
land and Tweedale are not the primary mountains, but
composed of the secondary schistus, which is every where
known to contain these objects belonging to the former
earth. Naturalists who have not an opportunity of convincing
themselves by their proper examination, must judge with
regard to that geological fact by the description of others.
Now it is most fortunate for natural history, that it has been
in this range of mountains that we have discovered those
marks of a marine origin: for, I shall afterwards have occasion
to give the clearest light into this subject, from observations
made in other parts of those same mountains of schist, by
which it will be proved that they are primary strata; and
thus no manner of doubt will remain in the minds of
naturalists, who might otherwise suspect that we were
deceiving ourselves, by mistaking the secondary for the
primitive schistus.

Remark that the
limestone is not
primitive,

Dr. Hutton's account of the mountains in the south of
Scotland is confused and unscientifical, and hardly comes
within the pale of *true geognosia*. It is not my intention, at
present, to enter into an examination of his observations;
the object of this postscript is to shew, that the limestone
between Noble House and the Crook Inn does not belong
to the primitive mountains. The beds of limestone mentioned
by Sir James Hall, I observed lying between strata of
transition slate, and this slate alternating with strata of grey
wacke; consequently the whole belongs to the transition
class of rocks.

for it lies between
strata of transition
slate; alternating
with strata of grey

The limestone has a blueish grey colour, fracture is foliated,
the distinct concretions are from coarse to fine grained, and

it is hardly translucid on the edges. It is often traversed by
veins of calcareous spar, and sometimes it contains thin beds
of flinty slate (Kiesel Schiefer of Werner). The transition slate
has a blueish or smoke grey colour, has generally less lustre
than the primitive slate, and contains much [interspersed]
mica. I observed it in all the stages from nearly pure slate
to grey wacke. The grey wacke is composed of fragments
of transition slate, flinty slate, and quartz, connected by a
basis of transition slate. It is frequently traversed by veins
of quartz, and is to be observed where the fragments are
hardly distinguishable from their size; it has much the
appearance of a breccia. I shall take another opportunity of
sending you drawings of the different kinds of petrefactions
that occur in the limestone.

wacke. Description
of the several rocks.

Chapter 15: The chemical revolution in four countries

15.1 S. Hales, *Vegetable Staticks*, 1727, London. Repr. Sci. Book Guild, 1961, pp. 89–95

The excellent Mr. *Boyle* made many Experiments on the Air, and among other discoveries, found that a good quantity of Air was producible from Vegetables, by putting Grapes, Plums, Gooseberries, Cherries, Pease, and several other sorts of fruits and grains into exhausted and unexhausted receivers, where they continued for several days emitting great quantities of Air.

Being desirous to make some further researches into this matter, and to find what proportion of this Air I could obtain out of the different substances in which it was lodged and incorporated, I made the following chymio-statical Experiments: For, as whatever advance has here been made in the knowledge of the nature of Vegetables, has been owing to statical Experiments, so since nature, in all her operations, acts conformably to those mechanick laws, which were established at her first institution; it is therefore reasonable to conclude, that the likeliest way to enquire, by chymical operations, into the nature of a fluid, too fine to be the object of our sight, must be by finding out some means to estimate what influence the usual methods of analysing the animal, vegetable, and mineral kingdoms, has on that subtile fluid; and this I effected by affixing to retorts and boltheads hydrostatical gages, in the following manner, *viz.*

In order to make an estimate of the quantity of Air, which arose from any body by distillation or fusion, I first put the matter which I intended to distill into the small retort *r* (Fig. 33) and then at *a* cemented fast to it the glass vessel *a b*, which was very capacious at *b*, with a hole in the bottom. I bound bladder over the cement which was made of tobacco-pipe clay and bean flower, well mixed with some hair, tying over all four small sticks, which served as splinters to strengthen the joynt; sometimes, instead of the glass vessel *a b*, I made use of a large bolthead, which had a round hole cut, with a red hot iron ring at the bottom of it; through which hole was put one leg of an inverted syphon, which reached up as far as *z*. Matters being thus prepared, holding the retort uppermost, I immersed the bolthead into a large vessel of water, to *a* the top of the bolthead; as the water rushed in at the bottom of the bolthead, the Air was driven out thro' the syphon: When the bolthead was full of water to *z*, then I closed the outward orifice of the syphon with the end of my finger, and at the same time drew the other leg of it out of the bolthead, by which means the water continued up to *z*, and could not subside. Then I placed under the bolthead, while it was in the water, the vessel *x x*, which done, I lifted the vessel *x x* with the bolthead in it out of the water, and tyed a waxed thread at *z* to mark the height of the

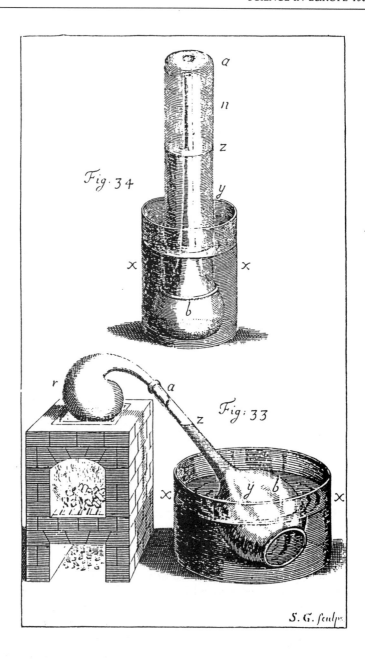

water: And then approached the retort gradually to the fire, taking care to screen the whole bolthead from the heat of the fire.

The descent of the water in the bolthead shewed the sums of the expansion of the Air, and of the matter which was distilling; The expansion of the Air alone, when the lower part of the retort was beginning to be red hot, was at a medium, nearly equal to the capacity of the retorts, so that it then took up a double space; and in a white and almost melting heat, the Air took up a tripple space or something more: for which reason the least retorts are best for these Experiments. The expansion of the distilling bodies was sometimes very little, and sometimes many times greater than that of the Air in the retort, according to their different natures.

When the matter was sufficiently distilled, the retort &c. was gradually removed from the fire, and when cool enough, was carried into another room, where there was no fire. When all was thoroughly cold, either the following day, or sometimes 3 or 4 days after, I marked the surface of the water y, where it then stood; if the surface of the water was below z, then the empty space between y and z shewed how much Air was generated, or raised from a fix'd to an elastick state, by the action of the fire in distillation: But if y the surface of the water was above z, the space between z and y, which was filled with water, shewed the quantity of Air which had been absorbed in the operation, i.e. was changed from a repelling elastick to a fix'd state, by the strong attraction of other particles, which I therefore call absorbing. [. . .]

I made use of the following means to measure the great quantities of Air, which were either raised and generated, or absorbed by the fermentation arising from the mixture of variety of solid and fluid substances, whereby I could easily estimate the surprising effects of fermentation on the air, viz.

I put into the bolthead b (Fig. 34) the ingredients, and then run the long neck of the bolthead into the deep cylindrical glass $a\,y$, and inclined the inverted glass $a\,y$, and bolthead almost horizontally in a large vessel of water, that the water might run into the glass $a\,y$; when it was almost up to a the top of the bolthead, I then immersed the bottom of the bolthead, and lower part y of the cylindrical glass under water, raising at the same time the end a uppermost. Then before I took them out of the water, I set the bolthead and lower part of the cylindrical glass $a\,y$ into the earthen vessel $x\,x$ full of water, and having lifted all out of the great vessel of water, I marked the surface z of the water in the glass $a\,y$.

If the ingredients in the bolthead, upon fermenting generated Air, then the water would fall from z to y, and the empty space zy was equal to the bulk of the quantity of Air generated: But if the ingredients upon fermentation did absorb or fix the active particles of Air, then the surface of the water would ascend from z to n, and the space $z\,n$, which was filled with water, was equal to the bulk of Air, which was absorbed by the ingredients, or by the fume arising from them: When the quantities of Air, either generated or absorbed, were very great, then I made use of large chymical receivers instead of the glass $a\,y$: But if these quantities were very small, then instead of the bolthead and deep cylindrical glass $a\,y$, I made use of a small cylindrical glass, or a common beer glass inverted, and placed under it a Viol or Jelly glass, taking care that the water did not come at the ingredients in them, which was easily prevented by drawing the water up under the inverted glass to what height I pleased by means of a syphon;
[. . .]

The illustrious Sir *Isaac Newton* (query 31st of his Opticks) observes, that 'true permanent Air arises by fermentation or heat, from those bodies which the chymists call fixed, whose particles adhere by a strong attraction, and are not therefore separated and rarified without fermentation. Those particles receding from one another with the greatest repulsive force, and being most difficultly brought together, which upon contact were most strongly united. And query 30. dense bodies by fermentation rarify into several sorts of Air; and this Air by fermentation, and sometimes without it, returns into dense bodies.' Of the truth of which we have evident proof from many of the following Experiments, *viz.*

That I might be well assured that no part of the new Air which was produced in distillation of bodies, arose either from the greatly heated Air in the retorts, or from the substance of the heated retorts, I first gave a red hot heat both to an empty glass retort and also to an iron retort made of a musket barrel; when all was cold, I found the Air took up no more room than before it was heated: whence I was assured, that no Air arose, either from the substance of the retorts, or from the heated Air.

15.2 J. Priestley, *Experiments and Observations on Different Kinds of Air*, 2 vols., 1775, London, vol. 2. Alembic Club Repr., 1947, no. 7. pp. 14–19 *passim*. Priestley's discovery of oxygen

Till this 1st of March, 1775, I had so little suspicion of the air from mercurius calcinatus, &c. being wholesome, that I had not even thought of applying to it the test of nitrous air; but thinking (as my reader must imagine I frequently must have done) on the candle burning in it after long agitation in water, it occurred to me at last to make the experiment; and putting one measure of nitrous air to two measures of this air, I found, not only that it was diminished, but that it was diminished quite as much as common air, and that the redness of the mixture was likewise equal to that of a similar mixture of nitrous and common air.

After this I had no doubt but that the air from mercurius calcinatus was fit for respiration, and that it had all the other properties of genuine common air. But I did not take notice of what I might have observed, if I had not been so fully possessed by the notion of there being no air better than common air, that the redness was really deeper, and the diminution something greater than common air would have admitted.

Moreover, this advance in the way of truth, in reality, threw me back into error, making me give up the hypothesis I had first formed, viz. that the mercurius calcinatus had extracted spirit of nitre from the air; for I now concluded, that all the constituent parts of the air were equally, and in their proper proportion, imbibed in the preparation of this substance, and also in the process of making red lead. For at the same time that I made the above mentioned experiment on the air from mercurius calcinatus, I likewise observed that the air which I had extracted from red lead, after the fixed air was washed out of it, was of the same nature, being diminished by nitrous air like common air: but, at the same time, I was puzzled to find that air from the red precipitate was diminished in the same manner, though the process for making this substance is quite different from that of making the two others. But to this circumstance I happened not to give much attention.

I wish my reader be not quite tired with the frequent repetition of the word *surprize*, and others of similar import; but I must go on in that style a little longer. For the next day I was more surprized than ever I had been before, with finding that, after the above-mentioned mixture of nitrous air and the air from mercurius calcinatus, had stood all night, (in which time the whole diminution must have taken place; and, consequently, had it been common air, it must have been made perfectly noxious, and intirely unfit for respiration or inflammation) a candle burned in it, and even better than in common air.

I cannot, at this distance of time, recollect what it was that I had in view in making this experiment; but I know I had no expectation of the real issue of it. Having acquired a considerable degree of readiness in making experiments of this kind, a very slight and evanescent motive would be sufficient to induce me to do it. If, however, I had not happened, for some other purpose, to have had a lighted candle before me, I should probably never have made the trial; and the whole train of my future experiments relating to this kind of air might have been prevented.

Still, however, having no conception of the real cause of this phenomenon, I considered it as something very extraordinary; but as a property that was peculiar to air that was extracted from these substances, and *adventitious*; and I always spoke of the air to my acquaintance as being substantially the same thing with common air. [. . .]

On the 8th of this month I procured a mouse, and put it into a glass vessel, containing two ounce-measures of the air from mercurius calcinatus. Had it been common air, a full-grown mouse, as this was, would have lived in it about a quarter of an hour. In this air, however, my mouse lived a full half hour; and though it was taken out seemingly dead, it appeared to have been only exceedingly chilled; for, upon being held to the fire, it presently revived, and appeared not to have received any harm from the experiment.

By this I was cofirmed in my conclusion, that the air extracted from mercurius calcinatus, &c. was, *at least, as good* as common air; but I did not certainly conclude that it was any *better*; because, though one mouse would live only a quarter of an hour in a given quantity of air, I knew it was not impossible but that another mouse might have lived in it half an hour; so little accuracy is there in this method of ascertaining the goodness of air: and indeed I have never had recourse to it for my own satisfaction, since the discovery of that most ready, accurate, and elegant test that nitrous air furnishes. But in this case I had a view to publishing the most generally-satisfactory account of my experiments that the nature of the thing would admit of.

This experiment with the mouse, when I had reflected upon it some time, gave me so much suspicion that the air into which I had put it was better than common air, that I was induced, the day after, to apply the test of nitrous air to a small part of that very quantity of air which the mouse had breathed so long; so that, had it been common air, I was satisfied it must have been very nearly, if not altogether, as noxious as possible, so as not to be affected by nitrous air; when, to my surprize again, I found that though it had been breathed so long, it was still better than common air. For after mixing it with nitrous air, in the usual proportion of two to one, it was diminished in the proportion of $4\frac{1}{2}$ to $3\frac{1}{2}$; that is, the nitrous air had made it two ninths less than before, and this in a very short space of time; whereas I had never found that, in the longest time, any common air was reduced more than one fifth of its bulk by any proportion of nitrous air, nor more than one fourth by any phlogistic process whatever. Thinking of this extraordinary fact upon my pillow; the next morning I put another measure of nitrous air to the same mixture, and, to my utter astonishment, found that it was farther diminished to almost one half of its original quantity. I then put a third measure to it; but this did not diminish it any farther: but, however, left it one measure less than it was even after the mouse had been taken out of it.

Being now fully satisfied that this air, even after the mouse had breathed it half an hour, was much better than common air; and having a quantity of it still left, sufficient for the experiment, viz. an ounce-measure and a half, I put the mouse into it; when I observed that it seemed to feel no shock upon being put into it, evident signs of which would have been visible, if the air had not been very wholesome; but that it remained perfectly at its ease another full half hour, when I took it out quite lively and vigorous. Measuring the air the next day, I found it to be reduced from $1\frac{1}{2}$ to $\frac{2}{3}$ of an ounce-measure. And after this, if I remember well (for in my *register* of the day I only find it noted, that it was *considerably diminished* by nitrous air) it was nearly as good as common air. It was evident, indeed, from the mouse having been taken out quite vigorous, that the air could not have been rendered very noxious.

For my farther satisfaction I procured another mouse, and putting it into less than two ounce-measures of air extracted from mercurius calcinatus and air from red precipitate (which, having found them to be of the same quantity, I had mixed together) it lived three quarters of an hour. But not having had the precaution to set the vessel in a warm place, I suspect that the mouse died of cold. However, as it had lived three times as long as it could probably have lived in the same quantity of common air, and I did not expect much accuracy from this kind of test, I did not think it necessary to make any more experiments with mice.

Being now fully satisfied of the superior goodness of this kind of air, I proceeded to measure that degree of purity, with as much accuracy as I could, by the test of nitrous air; and I began with putting one measure of nitrous air to two measures of this air, as if I had been examining common air; and now I observed that the diminution was evidently greater than common air would have suffered by the same treatment. A second measure of nitrous air reduced it to two thirds of its original quantity, and a third measure to one half. Suspecting that the diminution could not proceed much farther, I then added only half a measure of nitrous air, by which it was diminished still more; but not much, and another half measure made it more than half of its original quantity; so that, in this case, two measures of this air took more than two measures of nitrous air, and yet remained less than half of what it was. Five measures brought it pretty exactly to its original dimensions.

At the same time, air from the *red precipitate* was diminished in the same proportion as that from *mercurius calcinatus*, five measures of nitrous air being received by two measures of this without any increase of dimensions. Now as common air takes about one half of its bulk of nitrous air, before it begins to receive any addition to its dimensions from more nitrous air, and this air took more than four half-measures before it ceased to be diminished by more nitrous air, and even five half-measures made no addition to its original dimensions, I conclude that it was between four and five times as good as common air. It will be seen that I have since procured air better than this, even between five and six times as good as the best common air that I have ever met with.

Being now fully satisfied with respect to the *nature* of this new species of air, viz. that, being capable of taking more phlogiston from nitrous air, it therefore originally contains less of this principle; my next inquiry was, by what means it comes to be so pure, or philosophically speaking, to be so much *dephlogisticated*.

15.3 A. L. Lavoisier, *Elements of Chemistry* (*Traité Élémentaire de Chimie*, 1789), trans. R. Kerr (Edinburgh, 1790), reprinted Dover, 1965

CHAP. III.

Analysis of Atmospheric Air, and its Division into two Elastic Fluids; the one fit for Respiration, the other incapable of being respired.

FROM what has been premised, it follows, that our atmosphere is composed of a mixture of every substance capable of retaining the gasseous or aëriform state in the common temperature, and under the usual pressure which it experiences. These fluids constitute a mass, in some measure homogeneous, extending from the surface of the earth to the greatest height hitherto attained, of which the density continually decreases in the inverse ratio of the superincumbent weight. But, as I have before observed, it is possible that this first stratum is surmounted by several others consisting of very different fluids.

Our business, in this place, is to endeavour to determine, by experiments, the nature of the elastic fluids which compose the interior stratum of air which we inhabit. Modern chemistry has made great advances in this research; and it will appear by the following details that the analysis of atmospherical air has been more rigorously determined than that of any other substance of the class. Chemistry affords two general methods of determining the constituent principles of bodies, the method of analysis, and that of synthesis. When, for instance, by combining water with alkohol, we form the species of liquor called, in commercial language, brandy or spirit of wine, we certainly have a right to conclude, that brandy, or spirit of wine, is composed of alkohol combined with water. We can produce the same result by the analytical method; and in general it ought to be considered as a principle in chemical science, never to rest satisfied without both these species of proofs.

We have this advantage in the analysis of atmospherical air, being able both to decompound it, and to form it a new in the most satisfactory manner. I shall, however, at present confine myself to recount such experiments as are most conclusive upon this head; and I may consider most of these as my own, having either first invented them, or having repeated those of others, with the intention of analysing atmospherical air, in perfectly new points of view.

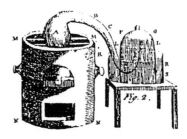

I took a matrass of about 36 cubical inches capacity, having a long neck B C D E, of six or seven lines internal diameter, and having bent the neck as in Plate so as to allow of its being placed in the furnace M M N N, in such a manner that the extremity of its neck E might be inserted under a bell-glass F G, placed in a trough of quicksilver R R S S; I introduced four ounces of pure mercury into the matrass, and, by means of a syphon, exhausted the air in the receiver F G, so as to raise the quicksilver to L L, and I carefully marked the height at which it stood by pasting on a slip of paper. Having accurately noted the height of the thermometer and barometer, I lighted a fire in the furnace M M N N, which I kept up almost continually during twelve days, so as to keep the quicksilver always almost at its boiling point. Nothing remarkable took place during the first day: The Mercury, though not boiling, was continually evaporating, and covered the interior furnace of the vessels with small drops, at first very minute, which gradually augmenting to a sufficient size, fell back into the mass at the bottom of the vessel. On the second day, small red particles began to appear on the surface of the mercury, which, during the four or five following days, gradually increased in size and number; after which they ceased to increase in either respect. At the end of twelve days, seeing that the calcination of the mercury did not at all increase, I extinguished the fire, and allowed the vessels to cool. The bulk of air in the body and neck of the matrass, and in the bell-glass, reduced to a medium of 28 inches of the barometer and 10° (54.5°) of the thermometer, at the commencement of the experiment was about 50 cubical inches. At the end of the experiment the remaining air, reduced to the same medium pressure and temperature, was only between 42 and 43 cubical inches; consequently it had lost about $\frac{1}{6}$ of its bulk. Afterwards, having collected all the red particles, formed during the experiment, from the running mercury in which they floated, I found these to amount to 45 grains.

I was obliged to repeat this experiment several times, as it is difficult in one experiment both to preserve the whole air upon which we operate, and to collect the whole of the red particles, or calx of mercury, which is formed during the calcination. It will often happen in the sequel, that I shall, in this manner, give in one detail the results of two or three experiments of the same nature.

The air which remained after the calcination of the mercury in this experiment, and which was reduced to $\frac{5}{6}$ of its former bulk, was no longer fit either for respiration or for combustion; animals being introduced into it were suffocated in a few seconds, and when a taper was plunged into it, it was extinguished as if it had been immersed into water.

In the next place, I took the 45 grains of red matter formed during this experiment, which I put into a small glass retort, having a proper apparatus for receiving such liquid, or gaseous product, as might be extracted: Having applied a fire to the retort in a furnace, I observed that, in proportion as the red matter became heated, the intensity of its colour augmented. When the retort was almost red hot, the red matter began gradually to decrease in bulk, and in a few minutes after it disappeared altogether; at the same time $41\frac{1}{2}$ grains of running mercury were collected in the recipient, and 7 or 8 cubical inches of elastic fluid, greatly more capable of supporting both respiration and combustion than atmospherical air, were collected in the bell-glass.

A part of this air being put into a glass tube of about an inch diameter, showed the following properties: A taper burned in it with a dazzling splendour, and charcoal, instead of consuming quietly as it does in common air, burnt with a flame, attended with a decrepitating noise, like phosphorus, and threw out such a brilliant light that the eyes could hardly endure it. This species of air was discovered almost at the same time by Mr. Priestley, Mr. Scheele, and myself. Mr. Priestley gave it the name of *dephlogisticated air*, Mr. Scheele called it *empyreal air*. At first I named it *highly respirable air*, to which has since been substituted the term of *vital air*. We shall presently see what we ought to think of these denominations.

In reflecting upon the circumstances of this experiment, we readily perceive, that the mercury, during its calcination, absorbs the salubrious and respirable part of the air, or, to speak more strictly, the base of this respirable part; that the remaining air is a species of mephitis, incapable of supporting combustion or respiration; and consequently that atmospheric air is composed of two elastic fluids of different and opposite qualities. As a proof of this important truth, if we recombine these two elastic fluids, which we have separately obtained in the above experiment, viz. the 42 cubical inches of mephitis, with the 8 cubical inches of respirable air, we reproduce an air precisely similar to that of the atmosphere, and possessing nearly the same power of supporting combustion and respiration, and of contributing to the calcination of metals.

Although this experiment furnishes us with a very simple means of obtaining the two principal elastic fluids which compose our atmosphere, separate from each other, yet it does not give us an exact idea of the proportion in which these two enter into its composition: For the attraction of mercury to the respirable part of the air, or rather to its base, is not sufficiently strong to overcome all the circumstances which oppose this union. These obstacles are the mutual adhesion of the two constituent parts of the atmosphere for each other, and the elective attraction which unites the base of vital air with caloric; in consequence of these, when the calcination ends, or is at least carried as far as is possible, in a determinate quantity of atmospheric air, there still remains a portion of respirable air united to the mephitis, which the mercury cannot separate. I shall afterwards show, that, at least in our climate, the atmospheric air is composed of respirable and mephitic airs, in the proportion of 27 and 73; [. . .]

I mentioned before, that we have two ways of determining the constituent parts of atmospheric air, the method of analysis, and that by synthesis. The calcination of mercury has furnished us with an example of each of these methods, since, after having robbed the respirable part of its base, by means of the mercury, we have restored it, so as to recompose an air precisely similar to that of the atmosphere. But we can equally accomplish this synthetic composition of atmospheric air, by borrowing the materials of which it is composed from different kingdoms of nature. We shall see hereafter that, when animal substances are dissolved in the nitric acid, a great quantity of gas is disengaged, which extinguishes light, and is unfit for animal respiration, being exactly similar to the noxious or mephitic part of atmospheric air. And, if we take 73 parts, by weight, of this elastic fluid, and mix it with 27 parts of highly respirable air, procured from calcined mercury, we will form an elastic fluid precisely similar to atmospheric air in all its properties.